# Math 1
## *An Incremental Development*

### Student Workbook (Part Two)

# Nancy Larson

with

## Linda Mathews

## Saxon Publishers, Inc.

*Math 1: An Incremental Development*

*Student Workbook*

Copyright © 1997 by Saxon Publishers, Inc. and Nancy Larson

Printed in the United States of America

ISBN 13: 978-0-939798-81-0 (set)
ISBN 13: 978-1-56577-448-3 (wb 1)
ISBN 13: 978-1-56577-449-0 (wb 2)

Editor: Deborah Williams
Production Supervisor: David Pond
Graphic Artists: Scott Kirby, John Chitwood, Gary Skidmore,
                 Tim Maltz, and Chad Threet

41 42 43 44 45  0304  26 25 24 23 22
4500844675

┌─ *Reaching us via the Internet* ─┐

**WWW:** www.saxonpublishers.com

**E-mail:** info@saxonpublishers.com

Name _____

+  _____

Total

+  _____

Total

+  _____

Total

+  _____

Total

$$
\begin{array}{r} 5 \\ -\ 0 \\ \hline \end{array}
\qquad
\begin{array}{r} 6 \\ -\ 6 \\ \hline \end{array}
\qquad
\begin{array}{r} 10 \\ -\ 5 \\ \hline \end{array}
\qquad
\begin{array}{r} 1 \\ -\ 0 \\ \hline \end{array}
\qquad
\begin{array}{r} 7 \\ -\ 1 \\ \hline \end{array}
$$

$$
\begin{array}{r} 14 \\ -\ 7 \\ \hline \end{array}
\qquad
\begin{array}{r} 5 \\ -\ 1 \\ \hline \end{array}
\qquad
\begin{array}{r} 7 \\ -\ 0 \\ \hline \end{array}
\qquad
\begin{array}{r} 4 \\ -\ 2 \\ \hline \end{array}
\qquad
\begin{array}{r} 9 \\ -\ 9 \\ \hline \end{array}
$$

$$
\begin{array}{r} 9 \\ -\ 1 \\ \hline \end{array}
\qquad
\begin{array}{r} 8 \\ -\ 0 \\ \hline \end{array}
\qquad
\begin{array}{r} 18 \\ -\ 9 \\ \hline \end{array}
\qquad
\begin{array}{r} 3 \\ -\ 3 \\ \hline \end{array}
\qquad
\begin{array}{r} 2 \\ -\ 0 \\ \hline \end{array}
$$

$$
\begin{array}{r} 16 \\ -\ 8 \\ \hline \end{array}
\qquad
\begin{array}{r} 3 \\ -\ 1 \\ \hline \end{array}
\qquad
\begin{array}{r} 5 \\ -\ 5 \\ \hline \end{array}
\qquad
\begin{array}{r} 6 \\ -\ 0 \\ \hline \end{array}
\qquad
\begin{array}{r} 12 \\ -\ 6 \\ \hline \end{array}
$$

$$
\begin{array}{r} 6 \\ -\ 1 \\ \hline \end{array}
\qquad
\begin{array}{r} 9 \\ -\ 0 \\ \hline \end{array}
\qquad
\begin{array}{r} 6 \\ -\ 3 \\ \hline \end{array}
\qquad
\begin{array}{r} 8 \\ -\ 8 \\ \hline \end{array}
\qquad
\begin{array}{r} 4 \\ -\ 1 \\ \hline \end{array}
$$

Score: _____

Name ● 
(Draw a line segment for your name.)

Date _____

Day of the Week _____

1. Write the number sixty-seven two more times. How many digits are on the line? _____

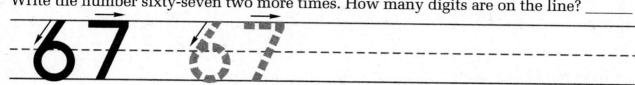

2. There were nine envelopes in the writing center. Ann used one envelope to send a letter to her mother. Draw a picture and write a number sentence to show the number of envelopes in the writing center now.

```
┌─────────────────────────────────────────────────────────┐
│                                                           │
│                                                           │
│                                                           │
│                                                           │
└─────────────────────────────────────────────────────────┘
```

Number sentence _____

How many envelopes are in the writing center now? _____ envelopes

3. Virginia made a pattern using the △green and ☐orange pattern blocks. Show a pattern Virginia could have made.

```
┌─────────────────────────────────────────────────────────┐
│                                                           │
│                                                           │
│                                                           │
└─────────────────────────────────────────────────────────┘
```

4. Write five different examples with a sum of 7.

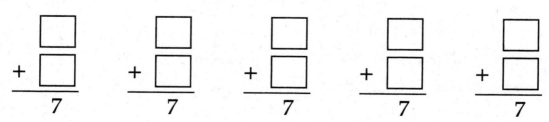

5. Use a crayon to circle all the even numbers in Problem 4.

Name _____

1.  Circle the one that is different.

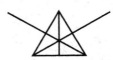  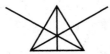 

2.  Uncle Eddie had 6 tennis balls. He lost one tennis ball when he hit it over the fence. Draw a picture and write a number sentence to show the number of tennis balls he has now.

    [ ]

    Number sentence _____

    How many tennis balls does Uncle Eddie have now? _____ tennis balls

3.  Jackie made a different pattern using the green and the orange pattern blocks. Show a pattern Jackie could have made.

    [ ]

4.  Write five different examples with a sum of 5.

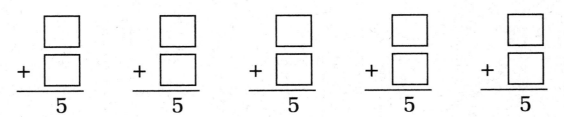

5.  Use a crayon to circle all the even numbers in Problem 4.

Name _____  **ASSESSMENT 14**

Date _____  **LESSON 75**

**Math 1**

1. Peggy counted six blue price tags and two yellow price tags. Draw the tags and write a number sentence to show the number of tags she counted.

    ┌─────────────────────────────────────────────┐
    │                                             │
    │                                             │
    │                                             │
    └─────────────────────────────────────────────┘

    Number sentence _____

    How many tags did Peggy count? _____ tags

2. What day of the week is it today? _____

3. Write a number word that has **3** letters. _____

    Write a number word that has **4** letters. _____

4. Write the answers.

    $\begin{array}{r} 5 \\ -\ 0 \\ \hline \end{array}$   $\begin{array}{r} 7 \\ -\ 7 \\ \hline \end{array}$   $\begin{array}{r} 9 \\ +\ 1 \\ \hline \end{array}$   $\begin{array}{r} 5 \\ +\ 2 \\ \hline \end{array}$   $\begin{array}{r} 8 \\ -\ 8 \\ \hline \end{array}$   $\begin{array}{r} 6 \\ -\ 0 \\ \hline \end{array}$   $\begin{array}{r} 8 \\ +\ 2 \\ \hline \end{array}$

5. Finish the pattern.

    45, 46, 47, _____ , _____ , _____ , _____ , _____ , _____ , _____

6. Number the clock face.

    Show two o'clock on the clocks.

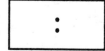

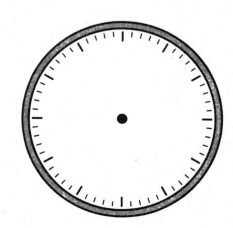

1-75Aa

+ _____

Total

+ _____

Total

+ _____

Total

+ _____

Total

| 2 | 2 | 3 | 1 | 2 |
|---|---|---|---|---|
| + 0 | + 6 | + 3 | + 9 | + 2 |

| 7 | 1 | 9 | 0 | 1 |
|---|---|---|---|---|
| + 7 | + 3 | + 9 | + 3 | + 1 |

| 0 | 4 | 1 | 4 | 6 |
|---|---|---|---|---|
| + 9 | + 4 | + 6 | + 2 | + 6 |

| 7 | 5 | 8 | 6 | 5 |
|---|---|---|---|---|
| + 1 | + 5 | + 0 | + 6 | + 1 |

| 8 | 2 | 3 | 8 | 2 |
|---|---|---|---|---|
| + 8 | + 7 | + 2 | + 1 | + 8 |

Score: _____

Name •
    (Draw a line segment for your name.)

Date _____

Day of the Week _____

1. Write the number sixty-eight two more times. How many digits are on the line? _____

2. Donald used 5 green pattern blocks and 3 blue pattern blocks to make a design. He took off 1 green pattern block. Draw a picture and write a number sentence to show how many green pattern blocks are in his design now.

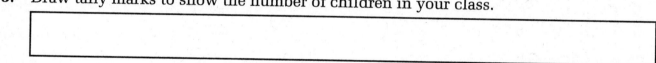

Number sentence _____

How many green pattern blocks are in his design now? _____ green pattern blocks

3. Draw tally marks to show the number of children in your class.

4. Choose **4 even** numbers.
Write them in the circles.
Add **1** to each number.
Find the answers.
Are the answers
even or odd numbers? _____

   ○      ○      ○      ○

   + 1    + 1    + 1    + 1

   □      □      □      □

5. How many dimes and pennies will you need to buy the ruler?

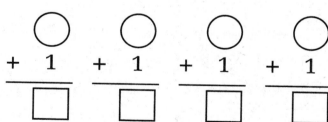

     _____ dimes      _____ pennies

6. Write the answers.

$6 - 0 =$ _____      $4 - 1 =$ _____      $14 - 7 =$ _____

$5 - 5 =$ _____      $6 - 3 =$ _____      $8 - 1 =$ _____

1. Fill in the missing numbers.

| | | | | | | 67 | | | |
|---|---|---|---|---|---|---|---|---|---|
| | | 74 | | | | | | | |

2. Elise used 6 green pattern blocks and 2 orange pattern blocks to make a design. She took off 1 green pattern block. Draw a picture to show how many green pattern blocks are in the design now.

Number sentence _____

How many green pattern blocks are in her design now? _____ green pattern blocks

3. Draw tally marks to show the number of people who live in your house.

How many tally marks did you draw? _____

4. Choose **4 odd** numbers.
Write them in the circles.
Add **1** to each number.
Find the answers.
Are the answers
even or odd numbers? _____

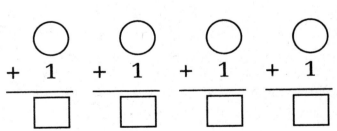

5. How many dimes and pennies will you need to buy the notebook?

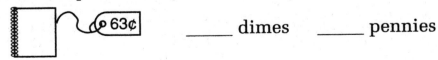 _____ dimes  _____ pennies

6. Write the answers.

$9 - 9 =$ _____    $8 - 4 =$ _____    $18 - 9 =$ _____

$5 - 1 =$ _____    $2 - 0 =$ _____    $7 - 1 =$ _____

Name _____

| | | |
|:---:|:---:|:---:|
| $\begin{array}{r} 4 \\ + 4 \\ \hline \end{array}$ | $\begin{array}{r} 4 \\ + 4 \\ \hline \end{array}$ | $\begin{array}{r} 4 \\ + 5 \\ \hline \end{array}$ |
| $\begin{array}{r} 7 \\ + 7 \\ \hline \end{array}$ | $\begin{array}{r} 7 \\ + 7 \\ \hline \end{array}$ | $\begin{array}{r} 7 \\ + 8 \\ \hline \end{array}$ |
| $\begin{array}{r} 5 \\ + 5 \\ \hline \end{array}$ | $\begin{array}{r} 5 \\ + 5 \\ \hline \end{array}$ | $\begin{array}{r} 5 \\ + 6 \\ \hline \end{array}$ |
| $\begin{array}{r} 3 \\ + 3 \\ \hline \end{array}$ | $\begin{array}{r} 3 \\ + 3 \\ \hline \end{array}$ | $\begin{array}{r} 3 \\ + 4 \\ \hline \end{array}$ |
| $\begin{array}{r} 6 \\ + 6 \\ \hline \end{array}$ | $\begin{array}{r} 6 \\ + 6 \\ \hline \end{array}$ | $\begin{array}{r} 6 \\ + 7 \\ \hline \end{array}$ |
| $\begin{array}{r} 8 \\ + 8 \\ \hline \end{array}$ | $\begin{array}{r} 8 \\ + 8 \\ \hline \end{array}$ | $\begin{array}{r} 8 \\ + 9 \\ \hline \end{array}$ |
| $\begin{array}{r} 2 \\ + 2 \\ \hline \end{array}$ | $\begin{array}{r} 2 \\ + 2 \\ \hline \end{array}$ | $\begin{array}{r} 2 \\ + 3 \\ \hline \end{array}$ |

Name _____

| | | | | |
|---|---|---|---|---|
| 2<br>+ 0 | 2<br>+ 6 | 3<br>+ 3 | 1<br>+ 9 | 2<br>+ 2 |
| 7<br>+ 7 | 1<br>+ 3 | 9<br>+ 9 | 0<br>+ 3 | 1<br>+ 1 |
| 0<br>+ 9 | 4<br>+ 4 | 1<br>+ 6 | 4<br>+ 2 | 6<br>+ 6 |
| 7<br>+ 1 | 5<br>+ 5 | 8<br>+ 0 | 6<br>+ 6 | 5<br>+ 1 |
| 8<br>+ 8 | 2<br>+ 7 | 3<br>+ 2 | 8<br>+ 1 | 2<br>+ 8 |

Score: _____

Name •
    (Draw a line segment for your name.)

Date _____

Day of the Week _____

1. Write the number sixty-nine three more times. How many digits are on the line? _____

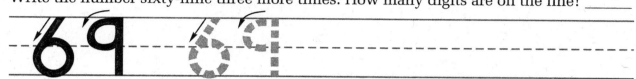

2. Louisa made a chain of paper clips. She used 6 large paper clips and 6 small paper clips. Draw a picture and write a number sentence to show Louisa's chain of paper clips.

   _____

   Number sentence _____

   How many paper clips did Louisa use in her chain? _____ paper clips

3. How many dimes and pennies will you need to buy the toy car?

    _____ dimes _____ pennies

4. Finish the pattern.

   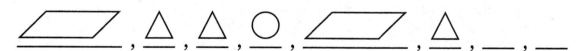

5. Christopher's receipt at the classroom store looked like this:

   How much money did he spend for the two items? _____

   How many dimes is that? _____

   How many pennies is that? _____

   | milk | | 42 | ¢ |
   |------|------|------|------|
   | beans | + | 31 | ¢ |
   | Total | | | ¢ |

Name _____     **LESSON 76B**
                                          **Math 1**

1.  Color the largest triangle blue.
    Color the second largest triangle red.
    Color the smallest triangle yellow.

2.  Paul made a chain of paper clips. He used 4 small paper clips and 8 large paper clips. Draw a picture and write a number sentence to show Paul's chain of paper clips.

    Number sentence _____

    How many paper clips did Paul use in his chain? _____ paper clips

3.  How many dimes and pennies will you need to buy the toy boat?

       _____ dimes   _____ pennies

4.  Finish the pattern.

    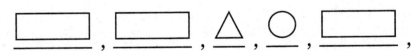

5.  Brendan's receipt at the classroom store looked like this.

    How much money did he spend for the two items? _____

    How many dimes is that? _____

    How many pennies is that? _____

| rolls | 14 | ¢ |
|---|---|---|
| corn | + 40 | ¢ |
| Total | | ¢ |

Circle the doubles plus one facts.

$5 + 6 =$ _____     $2 + 7 =$ _____     $3 + 4 =$ _____

$1 + 9 =$ _____     $8 + 7 =$ _____     $2 + 3 =$ _____

$6 + 0 =$ _____     $9 + 8 =$ _____     $5 + 4 =$ _____

$$\begin{array}{r} 3 \\ +\ 4 \\ \hline \end{array} \qquad \begin{array}{r} 7 \\ +\ 8 \\ \hline \end{array} \qquad \begin{array}{r} 2 \\ +\ 6 \\ \hline \end{array} \qquad \begin{array}{r} 1 \\ +\ 7 \\ \hline \end{array} \qquad \begin{array}{r} 2 \\ +\ 5 \\ \hline \end{array}$$

$$\begin{array}{r} 9 \\ +\ 7 \\ \hline \end{array} \qquad \begin{array}{r} 6 \\ +\ 5 \\ \hline \end{array} \qquad \begin{array}{r} 4 \\ +\ 8 \\ \hline \end{array} \qquad \begin{array}{r} 9 \\ +\ 8 \\ \hline \end{array} \qquad \begin{array}{r} 7 \\ +\ 5 \\ \hline \end{array}$$

$$\begin{array}{r} 5 \\ -\ 0 \\ \hline \end{array} \qquad \begin{array}{r} 6 \\ -\ 6 \\ \hline \end{array} \qquad \begin{array}{r} 10 \\ -\ 5 \\ \hline \end{array} \qquad \begin{array}{r} 1 \\ -\ 0 \\ \hline \end{array} \qquad \begin{array}{r} 7 \\ -\ 1 \\ \hline \end{array}$$

$$\begin{array}{r} 14 \\ -\ 7 \\ \hline \end{array} \qquad \begin{array}{r} 5 \\ -\ 1 \\ \hline \end{array} \qquad \begin{array}{r} 7 \\ -\ 0 \\ \hline \end{array} \qquad \begin{array}{r} 4 \\ -\ 2 \\ \hline \end{array} \qquad \begin{array}{r} 9 \\ -\ 9 \\ \hline \end{array}$$

$$\begin{array}{r} 9 \\ -\ 1 \\ \hline \end{array} \qquad \begin{array}{r} 8 \\ -\ 0 \\ \hline \end{array} \qquad \begin{array}{r} 18 \\ -\ 9 \\ \hline \end{array} \qquad \begin{array}{r} 3 \\ -\ 3 \\ \hline \end{array} \qquad \begin{array}{r} 2 \\ -\ 0 \\ \hline \end{array}$$

$$\begin{array}{r} 16 \\ -\ 8 \\ \hline \end{array} \qquad \begin{array}{r} 3 \\ -\ 1 \\ \hline \end{array} \qquad \begin{array}{r} 5 \\ -\ 5 \\ \hline \end{array} \qquad \begin{array}{r} 6 \\ -\ 0 \\ \hline \end{array} \qquad \begin{array}{r} 12 \\ -\ 6 \\ \hline \end{array}$$

$$\begin{array}{r} 6 \\ -\ 1 \\ \hline \end{array} \qquad \begin{array}{r} 9 \\ -\ 0 \\ \hline \end{array} \qquad \begin{array}{r} 6 \\ -\ 3 \\ \hline \end{array} \qquad \begin{array}{r} 8 \\ -\ 8 \\ \hline \end{array} \qquad \begin{array}{r} 4 \\ -\ 1 \\ \hline \end{array}$$

Score: _____

Name •
    (Draw a line segment for your name.)

Date _____

Day of the Week _____

1.  Write the number seventy 3 more times. How many digits are on the line? _____

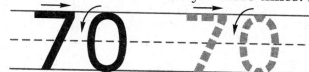

2.  Write a number word that has **4** letters.  ____  ____  ____  ____

    Write a number word that has **5** letters.  ____  ____  ____  ____  ____

    Write a number sentence to show how
    many letters you wrote altogether.  _____

    How many letters are in the two number words altogether? _____ letters

3.  Color the bottom half of
    the right-hand circle blue.

    Color the top half of
    the middle circle yellow.

    Color the top half of the left-hand circle red.

4.  Show four o'clock on the clocks.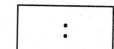

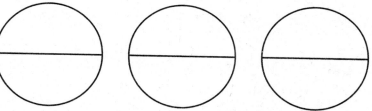

5.  Measure this line segment using pennies.

    _____ pennies

6.  Warren's receipt at the classroom
    store looked like this.

    How much money did he
    spend for the two items? _____

    How many dimes is that? _____

    How many pennies is that? _____

| soap  |     | 40 | ¢ |
|-------|-----|----|---|
| tuna  | +   | 24 | ¢ |
| Total |     |    | ¢ |

1. Circle the number that is between 24 and 32.

   24 ☐ 32     | 16   34   23   27 |

2. Write a number word that has **3** letters.   ____ ____ ____

   Write a number word that has **4** letters.   ____ ____ ____ ____

   Write a number sentence to show how
   many letters you wrote altogether.   _____

   How many letters are in the two number words altogether? _____ letters

3. Color the top half of
   the middle circle green.

   Color the bottom half of
   the right-hand circle red.

   Color the bottom half of
   the left-hand circle blue.

   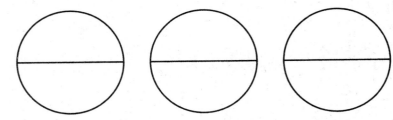

4. Show seven o'clock on the clocks.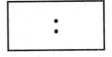

5. Measure this line segment using pennies.

   _____ pennies

6. Simon's receipt at the classroom
   store looked like this.

   How much money did he
   spend for the two items? _____

   How many dimes is that? _____

   How many pennies is that? _____

   | juice | 32 | ¢ |
   |---|---|---|
   | noodles + | 20 | ¢ |
   | Total | ☐ | ¢ |

$$\begin{array}{r} 5 \\ -\ 0 \\ \hline \end{array} \qquad \begin{array}{r} 6 \\ -\ 6 \\ \hline \end{array} \qquad \begin{array}{r} 10 \\ -\ 5 \\ \hline \end{array} \qquad \begin{array}{r} 1 \\ -\ 0 \\ \hline \end{array} \qquad \begin{array}{r} 7 \\ -\ 1 \\ \hline \end{array}$$

$$\begin{array}{r} 14 \\ -\ 7 \\ \hline \end{array} \qquad \begin{array}{r} 5 \\ -\ 1 \\ \hline \end{array} \qquad \begin{array}{r} 7 \\ -\ 0 \\ \hline \end{array} \qquad \begin{array}{r} 4 \\ -\ 2 \\ \hline \end{array} \qquad \begin{array}{r} 9 \\ -\ 9 \\ \hline \end{array}$$

$$\begin{array}{r} 9 \\ -\ 1 \\ \hline \end{array} \qquad \begin{array}{r} 8 \\ -\ 0 \\ \hline \end{array} \qquad \begin{array}{r} 18 \\ -\ 9 \\ \hline \end{array} \qquad \begin{array}{r} 3 \\ -\ 3 \\ \hline \end{array} \qquad \begin{array}{r} 2 \\ -\ 0 \\ \hline \end{array}$$

$$\begin{array}{r} 16 \\ -\ 8 \\ \hline \end{array} \qquad \begin{array}{r} 3 \\ -\ 1 \\ \hline \end{array} \qquad \begin{array}{r} 5 \\ -\ 5 \\ \hline \end{array} \qquad \begin{array}{r} 6 \\ -\ 0 \\ \hline \end{array} \qquad \begin{array}{r} 12 \\ -\ 6 \\ \hline \end{array}$$

$$\begin{array}{r} 6 \\ -\ 1 \\ \hline \end{array} \qquad \begin{array}{r} 9 \\ -\ 0 \\ \hline \end{array} \qquad \begin{array}{r} 6 \\ -\ 3 \\ \hline \end{array} \qquad \begin{array}{r} 8 \\ -\ 8 \\ \hline \end{array} \qquad \begin{array}{r} 4 \\ -\ 1 \\ \hline \end{array}$$

Score: _____

Name •
  (Draw a line segment for your name.)

Date _____

Day of the Week _____

1.  Write the number seventy-one four more times. How many digits are on the line? _____

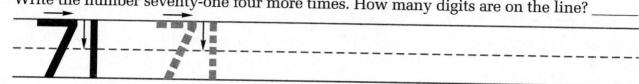

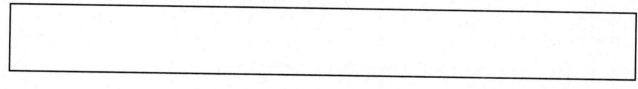

2.  Doreen had 6 dimes. She gave Harvey a dime. Draw a picture and write a number sentence to show the dimes Doreen has now.

    ┌─────────────────────────────────────────────────┐
    │                                                   │
    │                                                   │
    │                                                   │
    │                                                   │
    └─────────────────────────────────────────────────┘

    Number sentence _____

    How many dimes does Doreen have now? _____ dimes

    How much money is that? _____

3.  Write four number words that have four letters.

4.  Choose **4 odd** numbers.
    Write them in the circles.
    Add **2**.
    Find the answers.

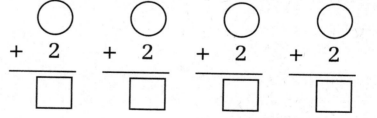

    Are the answers
    even or odd numbers? _____

5.  Show eleven o'clock on the clocks.

6.  Write the answers.

    $6 - 6 =$ _____        $4 - 1 =$ _____

    $5 - 0 =$ _____        $16 - 8 =$ _____

-78Wa

1. Write a number that is between 19 and 25.

19 ☐ 25

2. Melissa had 8 dimes. She gave Lena 2 dimes. Draw a picture and write a number sentence to show the dimes Melissa has now.

Number sentence _____

How many dimes does Melissa have now? _____ dimes

How much money is this? _____

3. Write four number words that have three letters.

☐ __ __ __    ☐ __ __ __ __    ☐ __ __ __ __    ☐ __ __ __ __

4. Choose **4 even** numbers.
   Write them in the circles.
   Add **2**.
   Find the answers.

   ○        ○        ○        ○
   + 2      + 2      + 2      + 2
   ☐        ☐        ☐        ☐

   Are the answers
   even or odd numbers? _____

5. Show ten o'clock on the clocks.

   ☐ : ☐

6. Write the answers.

   $8 - 8 =$ ____        $9 - 0 =$ ____

   $14 - 7 =$ ____        $9 - 1 =$ ____

| 3 | 5 | 2 | 7 | 4 |
|---|---|---|---|---|
| + 4 | + 6 | + 3 | + 8 | + 5 |

| 8 | 6 | 5 | 4 | 2 |
|---|---|---|---|---|
| + 9 | + 7 | + 6 | + 5 | + 3 |

| 7 | 3 | 6 | 8 | 4 |
|---|---|---|---|---|
| + 8 | + 4 | + 7 | + 9 | + 5 |

| 6 | 4 | 9 | 5 | 7 |
|---|---|---|---|---|
| + 5 | + 3 | + 8 | + 4 | + 6 |

| 8 | 6 | 5 | 9 | 3 |
|---|---|---|---|---|
| + 7 | + 5 | + 4 | + 8 | + 2 |

Score: _____

Name •
(Draw a line segment for your name.)

Date _____

Day of the Week _____

1. Write the number seventy-two 2 more times. How many digits are on the line? _____

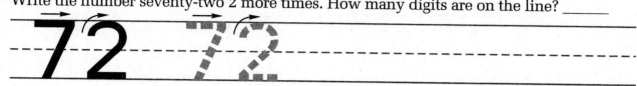

2. Mrs. Carrano has 5 pairs of earrings. Draw the earrings.

[ ]

How many earrings does she have? _____ earrings

3. Divide the squares in half two different ways.

   Color one half of the left square red.

   Color one half of the right square blue.

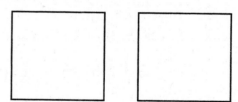

4. Draw tally marks to show the number of date tags on the calendar.

[ ]

How many tally marks did you make? _____ tally marks

5. Write the answers.

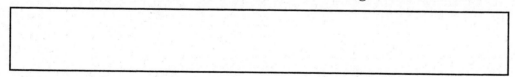

$$\begin{array}{cccccccc} 2 & 7 & 5 & 3 & 8 & 9 & 4 \\ +\,3 & +\,6 & +\,6 & +\,4 & +\,7 & +\,8 & +\,5 \\ \end{array}$$

Circle the sixth example using a red crayon.

Circle the third example using a blue crayon.

Name _____

1.  Fill in the missing numbers.

    1, 3, 5, _____ , _____ , _____ , _____ , _____ , _____

    66, 67, 68, _____ , _____ , _____ , _____ , _____ , _____

2.  Curtis has 4 pairs of shoes. Draw the shoes.

    ```
    ┌─────────────────────────────────────────────────┐
    │                                                   │
    │                                                   │
    │                                                   │
    │                                                   │
    └─────────────────────────────────────────────────┘
    ```

    How many shoes does he have? _____ shoes

3.  Divide the squares in half two different ways.

    Color one half of the left square green.

    Color one half of the right square yellow.

    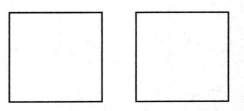

4.  Draw tally marks to show the number of windows in your house.

    ```
    ┌─────────────────────────────────────────────────┐
    │                                                   │
    │                                                   │
    │                                                   │
    └─────────────────────────────────────────────────┘
    ```

    How many tally marks did you make? _____ tally marks

5.  Write the answers.

    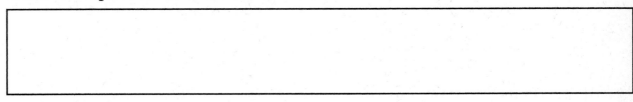

    $$8 + 7 \quad 5 + 4 \quad 4 + 3 \quad 5 + 6 \quad 8 + 9 \quad 6 + 7 \quad 3 + 2$$

    Circle the fourth example using a red crayon.

    Circle the second example using a blue crayon.

1.  Joan made 5 tally marks. Then she made 3 more tally marks. Draw the tally marks and write a number sentence to show how many tally marks she made altogether.

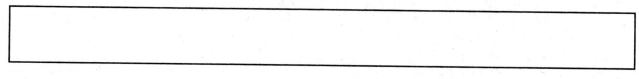

Number sentence _____

How many tally marks did she make altogether? _____ tally marks

2.  Circle the number that is between 34 and 43.

34 ☐ 43        33    38    44

3.  Color the bottom half of the left circle red.

Color the top half of the right circle green.

Color the bottom half of the right circle blue.

Color the top half of the left circle yellow.

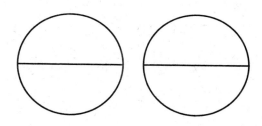

4.  How many dimes and pennies will you need to buy the book?

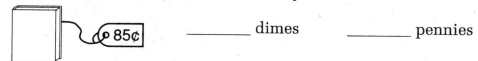

_____ dimes        _____ pennies

5.  Count by 5's. Fill in the missing numbers.

5, 10, 15, _____ , _____ , _____ , _____ , _____ , _____ , _____

6.  Write **3 even** numbers in the circles.
Add **1**.
Write the answers.

Are the answers
odd or even numbers? _____

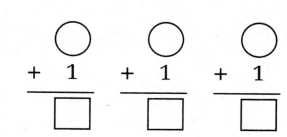

| | | | | |
|---|---|---|---|---|
| 3<br>+ 4 | 5<br>+ 6 | 2<br>+ 3 | 7<br>+ 8 | 4<br>+ 5 |
| 8<br>+ 9 | 6<br>+ 7 | 5<br>+ 6 | 4<br>+ 5 | 2<br>+ 3 |
| 7<br>+ 8 | 3<br>+ 4 | 6<br>+ 7 | 8<br>+ 9 | 4<br>+ 5 |
| 6<br>+ 5 | 4<br>+ 3 | 9<br>+ 8 | 5<br>+ 4 | 7<br>+ 6 |
| 8<br>+ 7 | 6<br>+ 5 | 5<br>+ 4 | 9<br>+ 8 | 3<br>+ 2 |

Score: _____

Name •
     (Draw a line segment for your name.)

Date _____

Day of the Week _____

1. Write the number seventy-three 3 more times. How many digits are on the line? _____

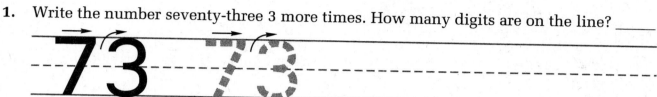

2. Jason counted five sunny day tags and three cloudy day tags. Draw a picture of the tags.

| Sunny | | | | | | |
|---|---|---|---|---|---|---|
| Cloudy | | | | | | |

How many more sunny days than cloudy days were there? _____ days

3. One of these numbers is my favorite number.
I will give you clues.
Cross out the numbers that can't be my favorite number.

It is not an even number.

It is not between four and six when you count by 1's.

Circle my favorite number.

| 5 | 7 | 10 |
|---|---|---|

4. How many tally marks are in the rectangle? _____

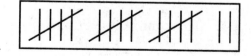

5. Joan's receipt at the classroom store looked like this:

How much money did
she spend for the two items? _____

How many dimes is that? _____

How many pennies is that? _____

| cereal | 24 | ¢ |
|---|---|---|
| milk + | 14 | ¢ |
| Total | | ¢ |

Name _____

1. Fill in the missing numbers.

    91, _____ , 93, _____ , 95, _____ , 97, _____ , 99, _____

2. Helen counted four sunny day tags and seven cloudy day tags. Draw a picture of the tags.

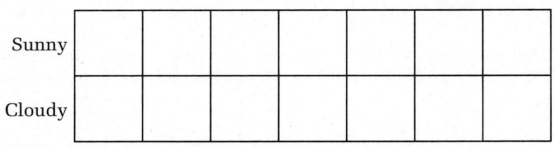

    Sunny

    Cloudy

    How many more cloudy days than sunny days are there? _____ days

3. One of these numbers is Donna's favorite number.
   Use the clues to find Donna's favorite number.
   Cross out the numbers that can't be her favorite number.

   It is not an odd number.

   | 4 | 5 | 8 |

   It is not between seven and nine when you count by 1's.

   Circle Donna's favorite number.

4. How many tally marks are in the rectangle? _____

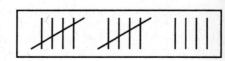

5. Mike's receipt at the classroom store looked like this:

   How much money did
   he spend for the two items? _____

   How many dimes is that? _____

   How many pennies is that? _____

   | cat food | 31 ¢ |
   |----------|------|
   | crackers + | 25 ¢ |
   | Total | ☐ ¢ |

$$3 + 4 \qquad 6 + 7 \qquad 9 + 8 \qquad 5 + 4 \qquad 7 + 8$$

$$6 + 5 \qquad 8 + 9 \qquad 4 + 3 \qquad 7 + 6 \qquad 4 + 5$$

$$8 + 7 \qquad 3 + 4 \qquad 5 + 4 \qquad 9 + 8 \qquad 5 + 6$$

$$6 + 7 \qquad 4 + 5 \qquad 7 + 8 \qquad 6 + 5 \qquad 8 + 9$$

$$3 + 4 \qquad 7 + 6 \qquad 5 + 6 \qquad 9 + 8 \qquad 8 + 7$$

Score: _____

Name ●
    (Draw a line segment for your name.)

Date _____

Day of the Week _____

1. Write the number seventy-four 4 more times. How many digits are on the line? _____

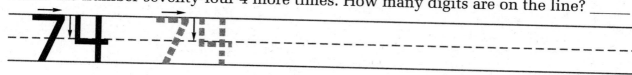

2. Four children said that blue is their favorite color.
Two children said that red is their favorite color.
Five children said that yellow is their favorite color.
Color the graph to show the children's favorite colors.

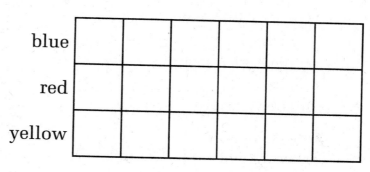

blue

red

yellow

Which color did the greatest number of children like? _____

Which color did the fewest number of children like? _____

How many more children like yellow than like red? _____

3. Divide each circle in half.
Color one half of the left circle green.

4. Write four different examples that have a sum of 4.

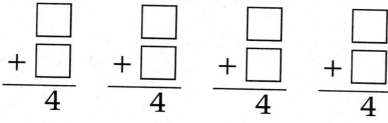

$$\begin{array}{r}\square\\[-2pt]+\ \square\\\hline 4\end{array}\qquad\begin{array}{r}\square\\[-2pt]+\ \square\\\hline 4\end{array}\qquad\begin{array}{r}\square\\[-2pt]+\ \square\\\hline 4\end{array}\qquad\begin{array}{r}\square\\[-2pt]+\ \square\\\hline 4\end{array}$$

5. Jed's receipt at the classroom store looked like this:

How much money did he spend for the two items? _____

How many dimes is that? _____

How many pennies is that? _____

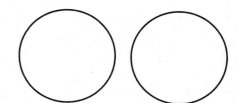

| yogurt | | 13 | ¢ |
|---|---|---|---|
| raisins | + | 34 | ¢ |
| Total | | | ¢ |

-82Wa

1. Fill in the mising numbers.

   10, 20, 30, _____ , _____ , _____ , _____ , _____ , _____ , _____

2. Three children said that orange is their favorite color.

   Six children said that green is their favorite color.

   Four children said that purple is their favorite color.

   Color the graph to show the children's favorite colors.

   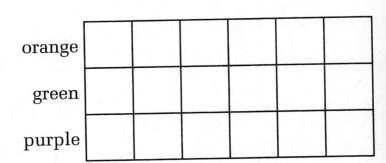

   Which color did the greatest number of children like? _____

   Which color did the fewest number of children like? _____

   How many more children like green than like purple? _____

3. Divide each circle in half.
   Color one half of the right circle red.

4. Write four different examples that have a sum of 5.

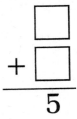   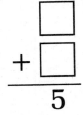   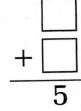

5. Carol's receipt at the classroom store looked like this:

   How much money did she spend for the two items? _____

   How many dimes is that? _____

   How many pennies is that? _____

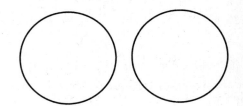

| beans | | 25 | ¢ |
| eggs | + | 24 | ¢ |
| Total | | | ¢ |

$$
\begin{array}{r} 3 \\ + 4 \\ \hline \end{array}
\qquad
\begin{array}{r} 6 \\ + 7 \\ \hline \end{array}
\qquad
\begin{array}{r} 9 \\ + 8 \\ \hline \end{array}
\qquad
\begin{array}{r} 5 \\ + 4 \\ \hline \end{array}
\qquad
\begin{array}{r} 7 \\ + 8 \\ \hline \end{array}
$$

$$
\begin{array}{r} 6 \\ + 5 \\ \hline \end{array}
\qquad
\begin{array}{r} 8 \\ + 9 \\ \hline \end{array}
\qquad
\begin{array}{r} 4 \\ + 3 \\ \hline \end{array}
\qquad
\begin{array}{r} 7 \\ + 6 \\ \hline \end{array}
\qquad
\begin{array}{r} 4 \\ + 5 \\ \hline \end{array}
$$

$$
\begin{array}{r} 8 \\ + 7 \\ \hline \end{array}
\qquad
\begin{array}{r} 3 \\ + 4 \\ \hline \end{array}
\qquad
\begin{array}{r} 5 \\ + 4 \\ \hline \end{array}
\qquad
\begin{array}{r} 9 \\ + 8 \\ \hline \end{array}
\qquad
\begin{array}{r} 5 \\ + 6 \\ \hline \end{array}
$$

$$
\begin{array}{r} 6 \\ + 7 \\ \hline \end{array}
\qquad
\begin{array}{r} 4 \\ + 5 \\ \hline \end{array}
\qquad
\begin{array}{r} 7 \\ + 8 \\ \hline \end{array}
\qquad
\begin{array}{r} 6 \\ + 5 \\ \hline \end{array}
\qquad
\begin{array}{r} 8 \\ + 9 \\ \hline \end{array}
$$

$$
\begin{array}{r} 3 \\ + 4 \\ \hline \end{array}
\qquad
\begin{array}{r} 7 \\ + 6 \\ \hline \end{array}
\qquad
\begin{array}{r} 5 \\ + 6 \\ \hline \end{array}
\qquad
\begin{array}{r} 9 \\ + 8 \\ \hline \end{array}
\qquad
\begin{array}{r} 8 \\ + 7 \\ \hline \end{array}
$$

Score: _____

Name •
(Draw a line segment for your name.)

Date _____

Day of the Week _____

1. Write the number seventy-five three more times. How many digits are on the line? _____

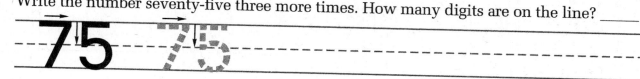

2. Eight children used a red crayon and ten children used a green crayon. Show on the graph how many children used each color.

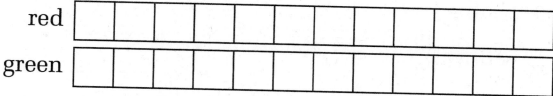

red

green

How many more children used green than red? _____ children

3. Color the congruent triangles red. (Congruent triangles are the same size and shape.)

  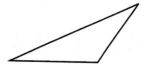 

4. Draw tally marks to show 25.

5. There are 8 sneakers in the closet.

   Draw the sneakers.

   Circle the pairs.

   How many pairs
   of sneakers are there? _____

   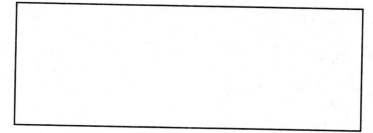

6. Write the answers.

| 8 | 6 | 3 | 8 | 9 | 3 | 12 | 5 | 14 |
|---|---|---|---|---|---|----|---|----|
| + 7 | + 5 | + 4 | + 9 | − 9 | − 1 | − 6 | − 0 | − 7 |

1-83Wa

1. Fill in the missing numbers.

| 41 |   | 43 |   | 45 |   | 47 |   | 49 |   |
| 51 |   | 53 |   | 55 |   | 57 |   | 59 |   |

2. Ten children used blue crayons and six children used yellow crayons. Show on the graph how many children used each color.

blue
|  |  |  |  |  |  |  |  |  |  |  |
|---|---|---|---|---|---|---|---|---|---|---|

yellow
|  |  |  |  |  |  |  |  |  |  |  |
|---|---|---|---|---|---|---|---|---|---|---|

How many more children used blue than used yellow? _____ children

3. Color the congruent rectangles blue. (Congruent rectangles are the same size and shape.)

4. Draw tally marks to show 20.

5. There are 10 boots inside the door.

   Draw the boots.

   Circle the pairs.

   How many pairs
   of boots are there? _____

6. Write the answers.

$$\begin{array}{cc} 2 \\ +\ 3 \\ \hline \end{array} \quad \begin{array}{cc} 8 \\ +\ 7 \\ \hline \end{array} \quad \begin{array}{cc} 4 \\ +\ 5 \\ \hline \end{array} \quad \begin{array}{cc} 6 \\ +\ 5 \\ \hline \end{array} \quad \begin{array}{cc} 6 \\ -\ 1 \\ \hline \end{array} \quad \begin{array}{cc} 8 \\ -\ 4 \\ \hline \end{array} \quad \begin{array}{cc} 7 \\ -\ 7 \\ \hline \end{array} \quad \begin{array}{cc} 18 \\ -\ 9 \\ \hline \end{array} \quad \begin{array}{cc} 2 \\ -\ 0 \\ \hline \end{array}$$

**10**

**10**

**10**

**10**

**10**

**10**

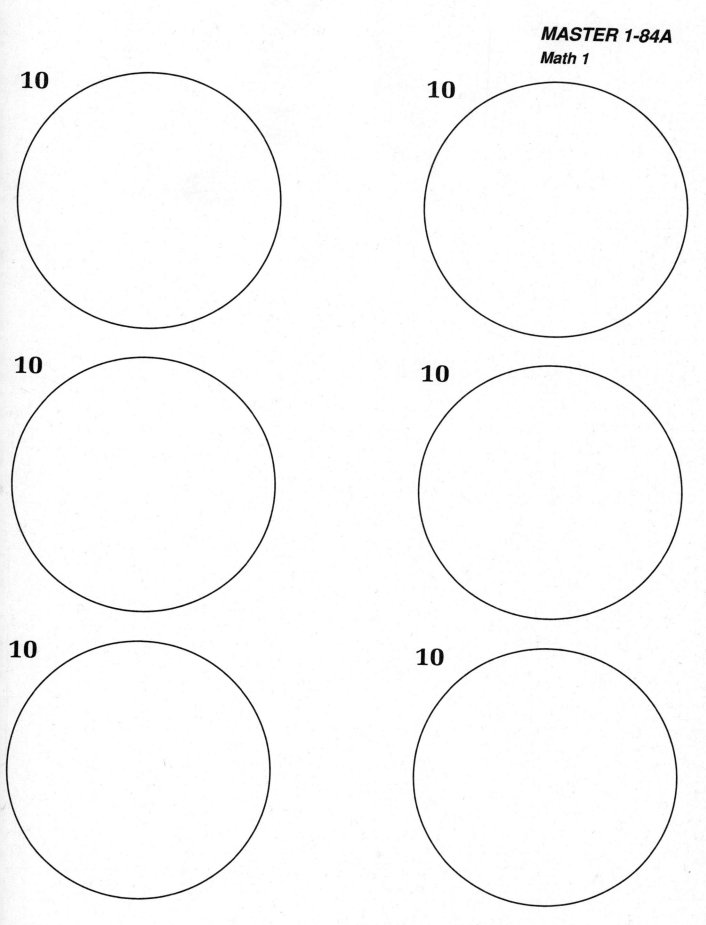

**10**

**10**

**10**

**10**

## Extras

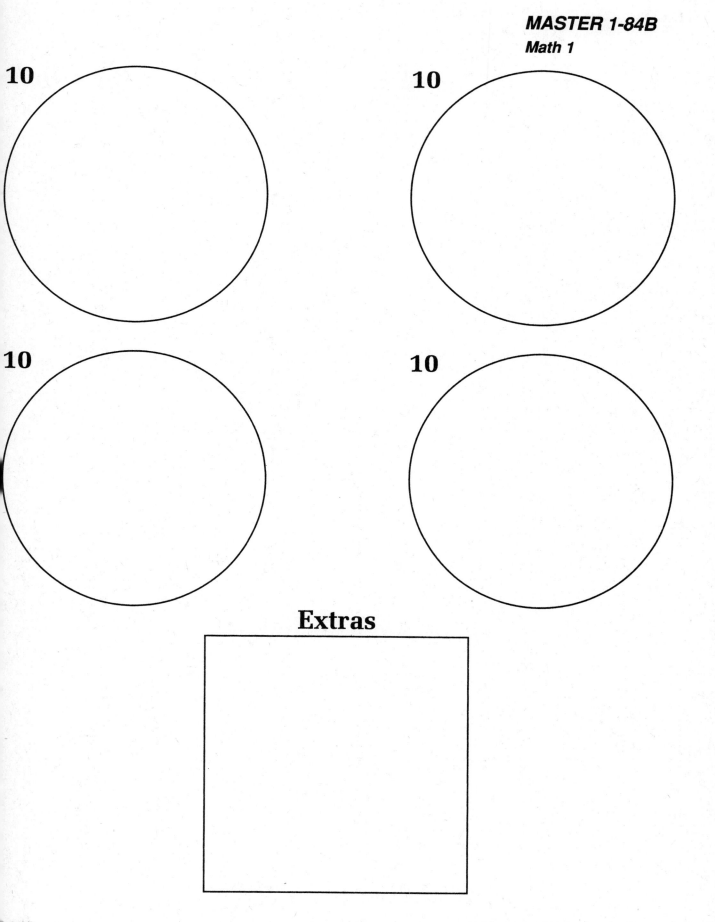

| | | | | |
|---|---|---|---|---|
| 3<br>+ 4 | 6<br>+ 7 | 9<br>+ 8 | 5<br>+ 4 | 7<br>+ 8 |
| 6<br>+ 5 | 8<br>+ 9 | 4<br>+ 3 | 7<br>+ 6 | 4<br>+ 5 |
| 8<br>+ 7 | 3<br>+ 4 | 5<br>+ 4 | 9<br>+ 8 | 5<br>+ 6 |
| 6<br>+ 7 | 4<br>+ 5 | 7<br>+ 8 | 6<br>+ 5 | 8<br>+ 9 |
| 3<br>+ 4 | 7<br>+ 6 | 5<br>+ 6 | 9<br>+ 8 | 8<br>+ 7 |

Score: _____

Name ●
 (Draw a line segment for your name.)

Date _____

Day of the Week _____

1. Write the number seventy-six two more times. How many digits are on the line? _____

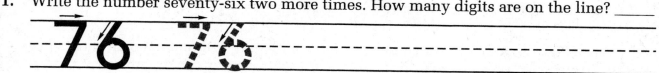

2. Write your first name. Put one letter in each square.

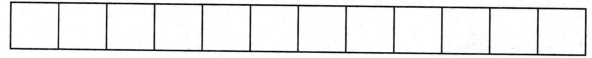

Write your last name. Put one letter in each square.

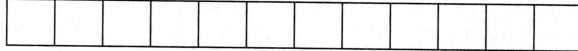

Which has more letters, your first or last name?   **first**   **last**   **same**

How many more letters does it have? _____ letters

3. Color the congruent shapes green.

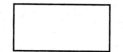     

4. Write the answers.

| 4 | 4 | 3 | 3 | 3 | 6 | 6 |
|---|---|---|---|---|---|---|
| + 4 | + 5 | + 0 | + 1 | + 2 | + 6 | + 7 |

5. Theresa's receipt at the classroom store looked like this:

How much money did
she spend for the two items? _____

How many dimes is that? _____

How many pennies is that? _____

| cake mix | 18 | ¢ |
|---|---|---|
| juice    + | 41 | ¢ |
| Total | | ¢ |

-84Wa

1. Circle the number that is between 24 and 26.

   | 23 | 24 | 25 | 26 | 27 | 28 |
   |----|----|----|----|----|----|

2. Write the first name of someone who lives with you. Put one letter in each square.

   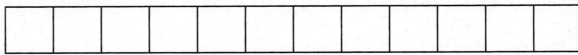

   Write that person's last name. Put one letter in each square.

   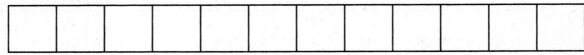

   Which has more letters, their first or last name?    **first    last    same**

   How many more letters does it have? _____ letters

3. Color the congruent shapes green.

4. Write the answers.

   $$\begin{array}{ccccccc} 3 & 3 & 8 & 8 & 8 & 5 & 5 \\ +3 & +4 & +0 & +1 & +2 & +5 & +6 \end{array}$$

5. Ted's receipt at the classroom store looked like this:

   How much money did
   he spend for the two items? _____

   How many dimes is that? _____

   How many pennies is that? _____

   | crackers | 22 | ¢ |
   |----------|----|---|
   | napkins + | 60 | ¢ |
   | Total | | ¢ |

Name _____

Date _____

Day of the Week _____

1. There were eight crackers on a plate. Phil ate four crackers. Draw a picture and write a number sentence to show what happened.

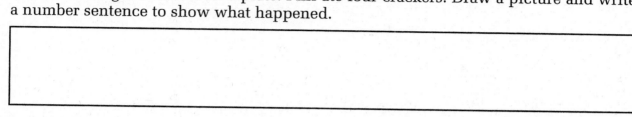

   Number sentence _____

   How many crackers are on the plate now? _____ crackers

2. Count the tally marks. How many tally marks are there? _____ tally marks

   Ⅲ Ⅲ Ⅲ |

3. Color the **X**, **Y**, and **Z** on this chart.

| 31 | 32 | 33 | 34 | 35 | 36 | 37 | 38 | 39 | Y |
|----|----|----|----|----|----|----|----|----|----|
| Z | 42 | 43 | 44 | 45 | 46 | 47 | 48 | 49 | 50 |
| 51 | 52 | 53 | 54 | 55 | 56 | 57 | X | 59 | 60 |

   What number belongs in the square with the **X**? _____

   What number belongs in the square with the **Y**? _____

   What number belongs in the square with the **Z**? _____

4. Divide the squares in half two different ways.
   Color one half of each square red.

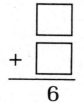

5. Write five different examples that have a sum of 6.

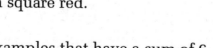

| | | | | |
|---|---|---|---|---|
| 6<br>+ 5 | 7<br>+ 1 | 9<br>+ 8 | 7<br>+ 7 | 3<br>+ 4 |
| 7<br>+ 8 | 0<br>+ 8 | 9<br>+ 1 | 3<br>+ 4 | 4<br>+ 5 |
| 5<br>+ 5 | 4<br>+ 2 | 6<br>+ 7 | 7<br>+ 2 | 8<br>+ 8 |
| 8<br>+ 7 | 5<br>+ 4 | 1<br>+ 8 | 2<br>+ 8 | 8<br>+ 9 |
| 2<br>+ 6 | 3<br>+ 2 | 9<br>+ 9 | 6<br>+ 7 | 7<br>+ 7 |

Score: _____

Name •
   (Draw a line segment for your name.)

Date _____

Day of the Week _____

1. Write the number seventy-seven 4 more times. How many digits are on the line? ____

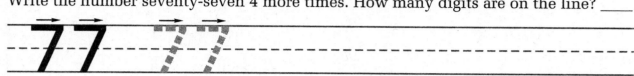

2. Four children chose chocolate milk.

   Three children chose white milk.

   Draw a picture of the glasses of milk on the graph.

| chocolate |  |  |  |  |
|-----------|--|--|--|--|
| white     |  |  |  |  |

   How many more children chose chocolate milk than chose white milk? _____ child

3. Annette put her beads on the string to make a pattern. Color the beads to show a pattern.

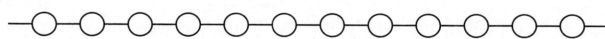

   What pattern did she make? _____

4. I have 14 pennies. Draw the pennies. Circle a group of 10 pennies.

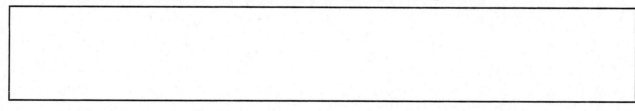

   If I trade 10 pennies for a dime, how many dimes and extra pennies will I have? _____ dime _____ pennies

5. Circle the doubles plus one addition examples. Write all the answers.

$$\begin{array}{ccccccc} 6 & 2 & 0 & 7 & 3 & 6 & 2 \\ +\,5 & +\,7 & +\,8 & +\,8 & +\,4 & +\,1 & +\,5 \\ \hline \end{array}$$

Name _____

1. Write the numbers that are one less and one more than each number.

   _____ , 16, _____          _____ , 27, _____          _____ , 49, _____

2. Two children chose grape juice.

   Four children chose orange juice.

   Draw a picture of the glasses of juice
   on the graph.

   | grape | | | | | |
   |-------|--|--|--|--|--|
   | orange | | | | | |

   How many more children chose orange juice than chose grape juice? _____ childrer

3. Vinny put his beads on the string to make a pattern. He made a different pattern tha
   Annette did. Color the beads to show a pattern.

   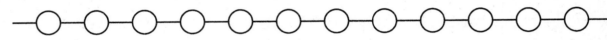

   What pattern did he make? _____

4. I have 17 pennies. Draw the pennies. Circle a group of 10 pennies.

   If I trade 10 pennies for a dime, how
   many dimes and extra pennies will I have? _____ dime _____ pennies

5. Circle the doubles plus one addition examples. Write all the answers.

$$\begin{array}{ccccccc} 9 & 4 & 1 & 2 & 6 & 2 & 9 \\ +\,2 & +\,5 & +\,7 & +\,0 & +\,7 & +\,6 & +\,8 \\ \hline \end{array}$$

Name _____

+ 

Total

+ 

Total

+ 

Total

+ 

Total

|  |  |  |  |  |
|---|---|---|---|---|
| 6<br>+ 5 | 7<br>+ 1 | 9<br>+ 8 | 7<br>+ 7 | 3<br>+ 4 |
| 7<br>+ 8 | 0<br>+ 8 | 9<br>+ 1 | 3<br>+ 4 | 4<br>+ 5 |
| 5<br>+ 5 | 4<br>+ 2 | 6<br>+ 7 | 7<br>+ 2 | 8<br>+ 8 |
| 8<br>+ 7 | 5<br>+ 4 | 1<br>+ 8 | 2<br>+ 8 | 8<br>+ 9 |
| 2<br>+ 6 | 3<br>+ 2 | 9<br>+ 9 | 6<br>+ 7 | 7<br>+ 7 |

Score: _____

Name •
(Draw a line segment for your name.)

Date _____

Day of the Week _____

1.  Write the number seventy-eight three more times. How many digits are on the line? _____

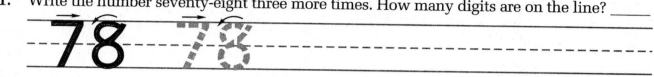

2.  Mrs. Dietsch counted six red shoes and eight blue shoes in the closet. Draw a picture and write a number sentence to show the shoes in the closet.

    ┌─────────────────────────────────────────────────────┐
    │                                                     │
    │                                                     │
    │                                                     │
    │                                                     │
    └─────────────────────────────────────────────────────┘

    Number sentence _____

    How many shoes are in the closet? _____ shoes

3.  William's receipt at the classroom store looked like this:

    How much money did
    he spend for the two items? _____

    How many dimes is that? _____

    How many pennies is that? _____

| pickles | 27 | ¢ |
|---------|----|----|
| pie   + | 31 | ¢ |
| Total   |    | ¢ |

4.  Sara put her pennies in groups of 10.

    How many pennies does she have? _____ pennies

    Sara traded the groups of pennies for dimes.

    How many dimes did she get? _____ dimes

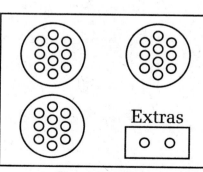

    o = penny

5.  Write the answers.

    $7 - 1 =$ _____        $16 - 8 =$ _____        $2 - 0 =$ _____

Name _____

1. Circle the one that is different.

2. Gary drew 7 small balls and 3 large balls. Draw a picture and write a number sentence to show the balls Gary drew.

Number sentence _____

How many balls did Gary draw? _____ balls

3. Mark's receipt at the classroom store looked like this:

How much money did
he spend for the two items? _____

How many dimes is that? _____

How many pennies is that? _____

| cake mix | 43 | ¢ |
|----------|----|----|
| napkins + | 36 | ¢ |
| Total | | ¢ |

4. Julie put her pennies in groups of 10.

How many pennies does she have? _____ pennies

Julie traded the groups of pennies for dimes.

How many dimes did she get? _____ dimes

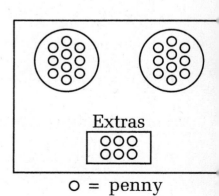

Extras

o = penny

5. Write the answers.

$5 - 0 =$ _____      $9 - 1 =$ _____      $5 - 5 =$ _____

| | | | | |
|---|---|---|---|---|
| 6<br>+ 5 | 7<br>+ 1 | 9<br>+ 8 | 7<br>+ 7 | 3<br>+ 4 |
| 7<br>+ 8 | 0<br>+ 8 | 9<br>+ 1 | 3<br>+ 4 | 4<br>+ 5 |
| 5<br>+ 5 | 4<br>+ 2 | 6<br>+ 7 | 7<br>+ 2 | 8<br>+ 8 |
| 8<br>+ 7 | 5<br>+ 4 | 1<br>+ 8 | 2<br>+ 8 | 8<br>+ 9 |
| 2<br>+ 6 | 3<br>+ 2 | 9<br>+ 9 | 6<br>+ 7 | 7<br>+ 7 |

Score: _____

1-87Fa

Name .
(Draw a line segment for your name.)

Date _____

Day of the Week _____

1. Write the number seventy-nine three more times. How many digits did you write? _____

2. Art put his crayons in groups of 10.

   How many crayons does he have? _____ crayons

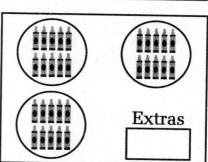

3. Show half past four on the clock.

4. This is Susan's receipt. Use dimes and pennies to find the total amount Susan spent.

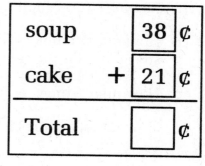

| | | |
|---|---|---|
| soup | 38 | ¢ |
| cake + | 21 | ¢ |
| Total | | ¢ |

5. Fill in the missing numbers.

   5, 10, 15, _____ , _____ , _____ , _____ , _____ , _____ , _____

6. How many dimes and pennies will you need to buy the apple?

   _____ dimes         _____ pennies

Name _____

1. Circle the number that is between 46 and 53.

   46 [ ] 53            | 41   57   45   52   44 |

2. Amy put her colored pencils in groups of 10.
   How many colored pencils does she have?

   _____ colored pencils

   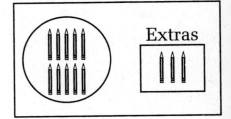

3. Show half past two on the clock.

4. Marsha's receipt at the classroom store looked like this:

   How much money did
   she spend for the two items? _____

   How many dimes is that? _____

   How many pennies is that? _____

   | cereal |   | 32 | ¢ |
   |--------|---|----|---|
   | cheese | + | 16 | ¢ |
   | Total  |   |    | ¢ |

5. Fill in the missing numbers.

   50, 45, 40, _____ , _____ , _____ , _____ , _____ , _____ , _____

6. How many dimes and pennies will you need to buy the orange?

   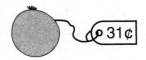

   _____ dimes            _____ penny

Name _____

|   6   |   7   |   9   |   7   |   3   |
|-------|-------|-------|-------|-------|
| + 5   | + 1   | + 8   | + 7   | + 4   |

|   7   |   0   |   9   |   3   |   4   |
|-------|-------|-------|-------|-------|
| + 8   | + 8   | + 1   | + 4   | + 5   |

|   5   |   4   |   6   |   7   |   8   |
|-------|-------|-------|-------|-------|
| + 5   | + 2   | + 7   | + 2   | + 8   |

|   8   |   5   |   1   |   2   |   8   |
|-------|-------|-------|-------|-------|
| + 7   | + 4   | + 8   | + 8   | + 9   |

|   2   |   3   |   9   |   6   |   7   |
|-------|-------|-------|-------|-------|
| + 6   | + 2   | + 9   | + 7   | + 7   |

Score: _____

Name •

(Draw a line segment for your name.)

Date _____

Day of the Week _____

1. Write the number eighty 2 more times. How many digits are on the line? _____

80  80  - - - - - - - - - - - - - - - - - - - - - - -

2. There were three pairs of skis in the closet. Sara put another pair of skis in the closet. Draw a picture of the skis in the closet. How many pairs of skis are in the closet now?

   _____ pairs

   How many skis is that? _____ skis

3. Draw lines to divide the squares into fourths two different ways. Color two fourths of each square.

4. Circle the one that doesn't belong.

5. Show half past nine on the clock.

6. Circle the even numbers on the clock.

7. Carol's receipt at the classroom store looked like this:

   How much money did she spend for the two items? _____

   How many dimes is that? _____

   How many pennies is that? _____

| muffins | 33 | ¢ |
|---------|----|----|
| jelly + | 42 | ¢ |
| Total | | ¢ |

-88Wa

1. Fill in the missing numbers.

| | 62 | | 64 | | 66 | | 68 | | 70 |
|---|---|---|---|---|---|---|---|---|---|
| | 72 | | 74 | | 76 | | 78 | | 80 |

2. There were four pairs of ice skates in the closet. Chris put another pair of ice skates in the closet. Draw a picture of the skates in the closet. Circle the pairs. How many pairs of ice skates are in the closet now?

   _____ pairs

   How many ice skates is that? _____ ice skates

3. Draw lines to divide the squares into fourths two different ways. Color one fourth of each square.

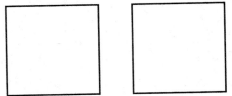

4. Circle the one that doesn't belong.

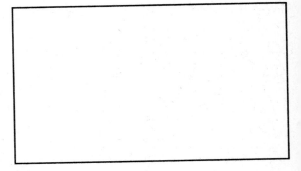

5. Show half past ten on the clock.

6. Circle the odd numbers on the clock.

7. Fred's receipt at the classroom store looked like this:

   How much money did he spend for the two items? _____

   How many dimes is that? _____

   How many pennies is that? _____

| soap | | 61 | ¢ |
|---|---|---|---|
| sponge | + | 17 | ¢ |
| Total | | | ¢ |

$$\begin{array}{r} 6 \\ +\ 5 \\ \hline \end{array} \qquad \begin{array}{r} 7 \\ +\ 1 \\ \hline \end{array} \qquad \begin{array}{r} 9 \\ +\ 8 \\ \hline \end{array} \qquad \begin{array}{r} 7 \\ +\ 7 \\ \hline \end{array} \qquad \begin{array}{r} 3 \\ +\ 4 \\ \hline \end{array}$$

$$\begin{array}{r} 7 \\ +\ 8 \\ \hline \end{array} \qquad \begin{array}{r} 0 \\ +\ 8 \\ \hline \end{array} \qquad \begin{array}{r} 9 \\ +\ 1 \\ \hline \end{array} \qquad \begin{array}{r} 3 \\ +\ 4 \\ \hline \end{array} \qquad \begin{array}{r} 4 \\ +\ 5 \\ \hline \end{array}$$

$$\begin{array}{r} 5 \\ +\ 5 \\ \hline \end{array} \qquad \begin{array}{r} 4 \\ +\ 2 \\ \hline \end{array} \qquad \begin{array}{r} 6 \\ +\ 7 \\ \hline \end{array} \qquad \begin{array}{r} 7 \\ +\ 2 \\ \hline \end{array} \qquad \begin{array}{r} 8 \\ +\ 8 \\ \hline \end{array}$$

$$\begin{array}{r} 8 \\ +\ 7 \\ \hline \end{array} \qquad \begin{array}{r} 5 \\ +\ 4 \\ \hline \end{array} \qquad \begin{array}{r} 1 \\ +\ 8 \\ \hline \end{array} \qquad \begin{array}{r} 2 \\ +\ 8 \\ \hline \end{array} \qquad \begin{array}{r} 8 \\ +\ 9 \\ \hline \end{array}$$

$$\begin{array}{r} 2 \\ +\ 6 \\ \hline \end{array} \qquad \begin{array}{r} 3 \\ +\ 2 \\ \hline \end{array} \qquad \begin{array}{r} 9 \\ +\ 9 \\ \hline \end{array} \qquad \begin{array}{r} 6 \\ +\ 7 \\ \hline \end{array} \qquad \begin{array}{r} 7 \\ +\ 7 \\ \hline \end{array}$$

Score: _____

Name ●
(Draw a line segment for your name.)

Date _____ ●

Day of the Week _____

1. Write the number eighty-one four more times. How many digits are on the line? _____

   81

2. There were ten library books on the table in Mrs. Sheehan's room. She took two books back to the library. Draw a picture and write a number sentence to show how many books are on the table now.

   Number sentence _____ Answer _____ library books

3. Draw lines to divide the rectangles in half two different ways. Color one half of each rectangle.

4. Draw tally marks to show 17.

5. Show the times on the clocks.

   three o'clock                    half past three

6. Add ten to each number.

| 80 | 27 | 43 | 51 | 18 |
|----|----|----|----|----|
|    |    |    |    |    |

Name _____

1.  Circle the largest number. Put an X on the smallest number.

| 54 | 34 | 63 |

2.  Marsha had five library books on her desk. She took four books back to the library. Draw a picture and write a number sentence to show how many library books are on her desk now.



Number sentence _____   Answer _____ library book

3.  Draw lines to divide the squares in half in two different ways. Color one half of each square.

4.  Draw tally marks to show 24.

5.  Show the times on the clocks.

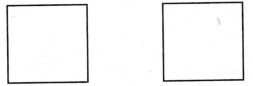

one o'clock            half past one

6.  Add ten to each number.

| 60 | 35 | 71 | 59 | 13 |

Name ●
    (Draw a line segment for your name.)

Date _____

Day of the Week _____

1. Write a number word that has **4** letters. _____

Write a number word that has **5** letters. _____

How many letters is that altogether? _____ letters

2. Draw tally marks to show 26.

3. Morgan counted seven sunny day tags and five cloudy day tags. Draw a picture of the tags.

    Sunny

    Cloudy

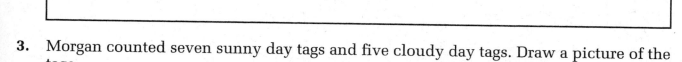

How many more sunny days
than cloudy days were there? _____ days

4. Quiana put the pencils in groups of 10.
How many pencils does she have?

_____ pencils

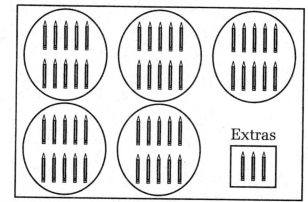

Extras

5. Eric's receipt at the classroom
store looked like this:

How much money did he
spend for the two items? _____

How many dimes is that? _____

How many pennies is that? _____

| cereal | 42 | ¢ |
|---|---|---|
| juice + | 25 | ¢ |
| Total | | ¢ |

6. Write the answers.

| 6 | 5 | 0 | 8 | 7 | 2 | 4 | 5 |
|---|---|---|---|---|---|---|---|
| + 2 | + 6 | + 3 | + 7 | + 1 | + 9 | + 3 | + 2 |

-90Aa

I can count by 10's, it's fun, it's fun. I can count by 10's and I'll start with one.

|  |  |  |  |  |  |  |  |  |  |
|--|--|--|--|--|--|--|--|--|--|
|  |  |  |  |  |  |  |  |  |  |

I can count by 10's, can you, can you? I can count by 10's and I'll start with two.

|  |  |  |  |  |  |  |  |  |  |
|--|--|--|--|--|--|--|--|--|--|
|  |  |  |  |  |  |  |  |  |  |

I can count by 10's, oh gee, oh gee. I can count by 10's and I'll start with three.

|  |  |  |  |  |  |  |  |  |  |
|--|--|--|--|--|--|--|--|--|--|
|  |  |  |  |  |  |  |  |  |  |

I can count by 10's, with numbers galore. I can count by 10's and I'll start with four.

|  |  |  |  |  |  |  |  |  |  |
|--|--|--|--|--|--|--|--|--|--|
|  |  |  |  |  |  |  |  |  |  |

I can count by 10's, like the bees in a hive. I can count by 10's and I'll start with five.

|  |  |  |  |  |  |  |  |  |  |
|--|--|--|--|--|--|--|--|--|--|
|  |  |  |  |  |  |  |  |  |  |

I can count by 10's, without any tricks. I can count by 10's and I'll start with six.

|  |  |  |  |  |  |  |  |  |  |
|--|--|--|--|--|--|--|--|--|--|
|  |  |  |  |  |  |  |  |  |  |

I can count by 10's, going up to heaven. I can count by 10's and I'll start with seven.

|  |  |  |  |  |  |  |  |  |  |
|--|--|--|--|--|--|--|--|--|--|
|  |  |  |  |  |  |  |  |  |  |

I can count by 10's, because in Math I'm great. I can count by 10's and I'll start with eight.

|  |  |  |  |  |  |  |  |  |  |
|--|--|--|--|--|--|--|--|--|--|
|  |  |  |  |  |  |  |  |  |  |

I can count by 10's, yes, I know I'm divine. I can count by 10's and I'll start with nine.

|  |  |  |  |  |  |  |  |  |  |
|--|--|--|--|--|--|--|--|--|--|
|  |  |  |  |  |  |  |  |  |  |

I can count by 10's, dear gentlemen. I can count by 10's and I'll start with ten.

|  |  |  |  |  |  |  |  |  |  |
|--|--|--|--|--|--|--|--|--|--|
|  |  |  |  |  |  |  |  |  |  |

| | | | | |
|---|---|---|---|---|
| 5<br>− 0 | 6<br>− 6 | 10<br>− 5 | 1<br>− 0 | 7<br>− 1 |
| 14<br>− 7 | 5<br>− 1 | 7<br>− 0 | 4<br>− 2 | 9<br>− 9 |
| 9<br>− 1 | 8<br>− 0 | 18<br>− 9 | 3<br>− 3 | 2<br>− 0 |
| 16<br>− 8 | 3<br>− 1 | 5<br>− 5 | 6<br>− 0 | 12<br>− 6 |
| 6<br>− 1 | 9<br>− 0 | 6<br>− 3 | 8<br>− 8 | 4<br>− 1 |

Score: _____

Name ●
    (Draw a line segment for your name.)

Date _____

Day of the Week _____

1. Write the number eighty-two three more times. How many digits are on the line? _____

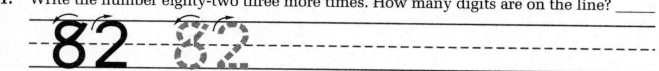

2. Write a story for the number sentence **4 + 1 = 5**.

    _____

    _____

3. Three children chose apples.
Five children chose oranges.
Draw a picture of the apples
and oranges on the graph.

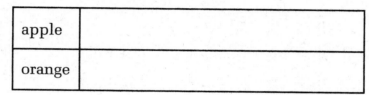

| apple | |
|-------|--|
| orange | |

◯ apple    ◯ orange

How many more children chose oranges than apples? _____ children

4. Draw lines to divide the squares into fourths in two different ways.

Color one fourth of each square.

☐    ☐

5. Count by 10's from 7. Fill in the numbers you say.

| 7 | | | | | | | | |
|---|---|---|---|---|---|---|---|---|

6. Write the answers.

   7 − 1 = ____      7 + 6 = ____      12 − 6 = ____

   6 + 2 = ____      8 − 0 = ____      4 + 5 = ____

1.  Write a number that is between 49 and 55.

2.  Write a story for the number sentence **1 + 5 = 6**.

    _____

    _____

3.  Four children chose peaches. Five children chose bananas. Draw a picture of the peaches and bananas on the graph.

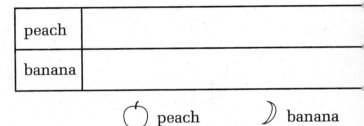

    How many more children chose bananas than peaches? _____ child

4.  Draw lines to divide the squares into fourths in two different ways.

    Color three fourths of each square.

5.  Count by 10's from 8. Fill in the numbers you say.

    | 8 | | | | | | | | | |
    |---|---|---|---|---|---|---|---|---|---|

6.  Write the answers.

    9 − 1 = ____        8 + 9 = ____        14 − 7 = ____

    7 + 2 = ____        5 − 0 = ____        6 + 5 = ____

Name _____

$$
\begin{array}{r} 5 \\ -\ 0 \\ \hline \end{array}
\qquad
\begin{array}{r} 6 \\ -\ 6 \\ \hline \end{array}
\qquad
\begin{array}{r} 10 \\ -\ 5 \\ \hline \end{array}
\qquad
\begin{array}{r} 1 \\ -\ 0 \\ \hline \end{array}
\qquad
\begin{array}{r} 7 \\ -\ 1 \\ \hline \end{array}
$$

$$
\begin{array}{r} 14 \\ -\ 7 \\ \hline \end{array}
\qquad
\begin{array}{r} 5 \\ -\ 1 \\ \hline \end{array}
\qquad
\begin{array}{r} 7 \\ -\ 0 \\ \hline \end{array}
\qquad
\begin{array}{r} 4 \\ -\ 2 \\ \hline \end{array}
\qquad
\begin{array}{r} 9 \\ -\ 9 \\ \hline \end{array}
$$

$$
\begin{array}{r} 9 \\ -\ 1 \\ \hline \end{array}
\qquad
\begin{array}{r} 8 \\ -\ 0 \\ \hline \end{array}
\qquad
\begin{array}{r} 18 \\ -\ 9 \\ \hline \end{array}
\qquad
\begin{array}{r} 3 \\ -\ 3 \\ \hline \end{array}
\qquad
\begin{array}{r} 2 \\ -\ 0 \\ \hline \end{array}
$$

$$
\begin{array}{r} 16 \\ -\ 8 \\ \hline \end{array}
\qquad
\begin{array}{r} 3 \\ -\ 1 \\ \hline \end{array}
\qquad
\begin{array}{r} 5 \\ -\ 5 \\ \hline \end{array}
\qquad
\begin{array}{r} 6 \\ -\ 0 \\ \hline \end{array}
\qquad
\begin{array}{r} 12 \\ -\ 6 \\ \hline \end{array}
$$

$$
\begin{array}{r} 6 \\ -\ 1 \\ \hline \end{array}
\qquad
\begin{array}{r} 9 \\ -\ 0 \\ \hline \end{array}
\qquad
\begin{array}{r} 6 \\ -\ 3 \\ \hline \end{array}
\qquad
\begin{array}{r} 8 \\ -\ 8 \\ \hline \end{array}
\qquad
\begin{array}{r} 4 \\ -\ 1 \\ \hline \end{array}
$$

Score: _____

Name _____

Date _____

Day of the Week _____

1. Write the number eighty-three three more times. How many digits did you use? _____

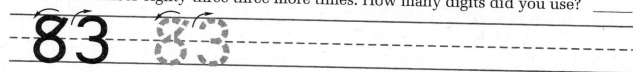

2. Write a number word that has exactly two vowels. _____

Write another number word that has exactly two vowels. _____
Write a number sentence to show how many letters you wrote.

Number sentence _____

How many letters is that? _____ letters

3. Color the pennies brown. How much money is this? _____

4. Circle the shapes that are divided into fourths (four equal pieces).

5. Show the number of lights in your classroom using tally marks.

How many tally marks did you draw? _____

6. Add 10 to each number.

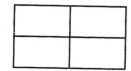 

| 63¢ | 29¢ | 16¢ |
|-----|-----|-----|
| + 10¢ | + 10¢ | + 10¢ |

Name _____

**LESSON 92B**

*Math 1*

1.  Circle the largest number.
    Put an X on the smallest number.

    | 53   42   50   37 |

2.  Use the words on this side of the paper.
    Write a word that has exactly two vowels. _____

    Write another word that has exactly two vowels. _____
    Write a number sentence to show how many letters you wrote.

    Number sentence _____

    How many letters is that? _____ letters

3.  Color the pennies brown. How much money is this? _____

4.  Circle the shapes that are divided into halves (two equal pieces).

5.  Show the number of chairs in your house using tally marks.

    How many tally marks did you draw? _____

6.  Add 10 to each number.

    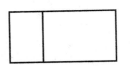   

$$\begin{array}{r} 54\text{¢} \\ +\ 10\text{¢} \\ \hline \end{array} \qquad \begin{array}{r} 38\text{¢} \\ +\ 10\text{¢} \\ \hline \end{array} \qquad \begin{array}{r} 14\text{¢} \\ +\ 10\text{¢} \\ \hline \end{array}$$

1-92Wb

$$\begin{array}{r} 6 \\ + 5 \\ \hline \end{array} \qquad \begin{array}{r} 7 \\ + 1 \\ \hline \end{array} \qquad \begin{array}{r} 9 \\ + 8 \\ \hline \end{array} \qquad \begin{array}{r} 7 \\ + 7 \\ \hline \end{array} \qquad \begin{array}{r} 3 \\ + 4 \\ \hline \end{array}$$

$$\begin{array}{r} 7 \\ + 8 \\ \hline \end{array} \qquad \begin{array}{r} 0 \\ + 8 \\ \hline \end{array} \qquad \begin{array}{r} 9 \\ + 1 \\ \hline \end{array} \qquad \begin{array}{r} 3 \\ + 4 \\ \hline \end{array} \qquad \begin{array}{r} 4 \\ + 5 \\ \hline \end{array}$$

$$\begin{array}{r} 5 \\ + 5 \\ \hline \end{array} \qquad \begin{array}{r} 4 \\ + 2 \\ \hline \end{array} \qquad \begin{array}{r} 6 \\ + 7 \\ \hline \end{array} \qquad \begin{array}{r} 7 \\ + 2 \\ \hline \end{array} \qquad \begin{array}{r} 8 \\ + 8 \\ \hline \end{array}$$

$$\begin{array}{r} 8 \\ + 7 \\ \hline \end{array} \qquad \begin{array}{r} 5 \\ + 4 \\ \hline \end{array} \qquad \begin{array}{r} 1 \\ + 8 \\ \hline \end{array} \qquad \begin{array}{r} 2 \\ + 8 \\ \hline \end{array} \qquad \begin{array}{r} 8 \\ + 9 \\ \hline \end{array}$$

$$\begin{array}{r} 2 \\ + 6 \\ \hline \end{array} \qquad \begin{array}{r} 3 \\ + 2 \\ \hline \end{array} \qquad \begin{array}{r} 9 \\ + 9 \\ \hline \end{array} \qquad \begin{array}{r} 6 \\ + 7 \\ \hline \end{array} \qquad \begin{array}{r} 7 \\ + 7 \\ \hline \end{array}$$

Score: _____

Name ●

Date _____

Day of the Week _____

1.  Write the number eighty-four four more times. How many digits did you use? _____

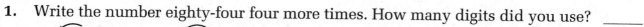

2.  Julie put five pairs of socks in the washing machine.
    Draw the socks in the washing machine.
    When she took the socks out of the washing machine,
    she counted eight socks. What happened?

    _____

    _____

3.  Put these number cards in order from least to greatest.

    | 25 | 42 | 13 | 31 |

    □   □   □   □
    least       greatest

4.  Color the pennies brown. How much money is this? _____

5.  Draw a triangle in the second square.
    Draw a circle around the sixth square.
    Put an X in the middle square.
    Divide the third square into halves.
    Divide the fifth square into fourths.

    □ □ □ □ □ □ □

6.  Show half past eleven on the clock.

    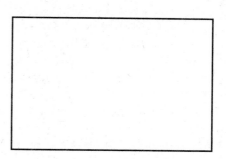

7.  Write the answers.

$$\begin{array}{cccccccc} 5 & 3 & 12 & 7 & 5 & 9 & 4 & 7 & 8 \\ +\,4 & -\,1 & -\,6 & +\,8 & +\,2 & -\,0 & +\,3 & -\,7 & +\,9 \\ \hline \end{array}$$

Name _____

1. Fill in the missing numbers.

   10, 20, 30, _____ , _____ , _____ , _____ , _____ , _____ , _____

   2, 4, 6, _____ , _____ , _____ , _____ , _____ , _____ , _____

2. Corrine put four pairs of socks in the washing machine.
   Draw the socks in the washing machine.
   When she took the socks out of the washing machine,
   she counted seven socks. What happened?

   _____

   _____

3. Put these number cards in order from least to greatest.

   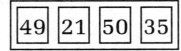

   [ ] [ ] [ ] [ ]
   least        greatest

4. Color the pennies brown. How much money is this? _____

   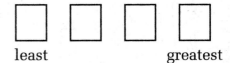

5. Draw a triangle in the last square.
   Draw a circle around the second square.
   Put an X below the fourth square.
   Divide the sixth square into fourths.
   Divide the middle square into halves.

6. Show half past one on the clock.

7. Write the answers.

   | 6 | 7 | 10 | 8 | 9 | 3 | 5 | 6 | 7 |
   |---|---|----|---|---|---|---|---|---|
   | + 5 | − 1 | − 5 | + 7 | + 2 | − 0 | + 4 | − 6 | + 6 |

$$\begin{array}{r} 3 \\ + \boxed{\phantom{0}} \\ \hline 10 \end{array} \qquad \begin{array}{r} 8 \\ + \boxed{\phantom{0}} \\ \hline 10 \end{array} \qquad \begin{array}{r} \boxed{\phantom{0}} \\ + 4 \\ \hline 10 \end{array} \qquad \begin{array}{r} 5 \\ + \boxed{\phantom{0}} \\ \hline 10 \end{array} \qquad \begin{array}{r} \boxed{\phantom{0}} \\ + 1 \\ \hline 10 \end{array}$$

$$\begin{array}{r} 2 \\ + \boxed{\phantom{0}} \\ \hline 10 \end{array} \qquad \begin{array}{r} 6 \\ + \boxed{\phantom{0}} \\ \hline 10 \end{array} \qquad \begin{array}{r} \boxed{\phantom{0}} \\ + 5 \\ \hline 10 \end{array} \qquad \begin{array}{r} \boxed{\phantom{0}} \\ + 3 \\ \hline 10 \end{array} \qquad \begin{array}{r} 9 \\ + \boxed{\phantom{0}} \\ \hline 10 \end{array}$$

$$\begin{array}{r} 7 \\ + \boxed{\phantom{0}} \\ \hline 10 \end{array} \qquad \begin{array}{r} \boxed{\phantom{0}} \\ + 1 \\ \hline 10 \end{array} \qquad \begin{array}{r} 5 \\ + \boxed{\phantom{0}} \\ \hline 10 \end{array} \qquad \begin{array}{r} 4 \\ + \boxed{\phantom{0}} \\ \hline 10 \end{array} \qquad \begin{array}{r} \boxed{\phantom{0}} \\ + 8 \\ \hline 10 \end{array}$$

$$\begin{array}{r} 9 \\ + \boxed{\phantom{0}} \\ \hline 10 \end{array} \qquad \begin{array}{r} \boxed{\phantom{0}} \\ + 2 \\ \hline 10 \end{array} \qquad \begin{array}{r} 6 \\ + \boxed{\phantom{0}} \\ \hline 10 \end{array} \qquad \begin{array}{r} \boxed{\phantom{0}} \\ + 5 \\ \hline 10 \end{array} \qquad \begin{array}{r} \boxed{\phantom{0}} \\ + 7 \\ \hline 10 \end{array}$$

$$\begin{array}{r} 1 \\ + \boxed{\phantom{0}} \\ \hline 10 \end{array} \qquad \begin{array}{r} \boxed{\phantom{0}} \\ + 6 \\ \hline 10 \end{array} \qquad \begin{array}{r} 3 \\ + \boxed{\phantom{0}} \\ \hline 10 \end{array} \qquad \begin{array}{r} 8 \\ + \boxed{\phantom{0}} \\ \hline 10 \end{array} \qquad \begin{array}{r} \boxed{\phantom{0}} \\ + 5 \\ \hline 10 \end{array}$$

Score: _____

Name _____  **LESSON 94A**

Date _____  *Math 1*

Day of the Week _____

1.  Write the number eighty-five three more times. How many digits did you use? _____

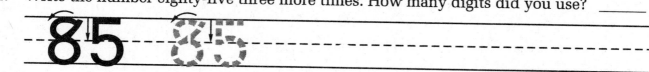

2.  Christa had 41¢. Show this using the fewest number of dimes and pennies.
    Color the pennies brown.

    She found another dime. Draw the dime.
    How much money does Christa have now? _____

3.  Someone made a mistake when they put these number cards in order. Circle a
    number card that you would move so that the number cards will be in order.

    | 7 | 12 | 16 | 24 | 21 | 27 | 35 |

4.  Color the even numbers yellow in Problem 3.

5.  Fill in the missing numbers.

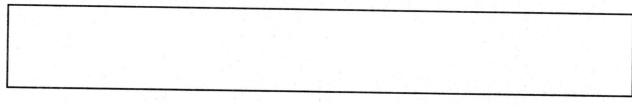

6.  Ask exactly 10 people whether they like the color red or the color blue better.
    Show their choice on this graph.

    red

    blue

    Which color did most of the people you asked like better? _____

1. Write a number that is between 29 and 35 when you count by 1's.

   29 ☐ 35

2. Dan had 32¢. Show this using the fewest number of dimes and pennies.
   Color the pennies brown.

   ┌─────────────────────────────────────────┐
   │                                           │
   │                                           │
   │                                           │
   └─────────────────────────────────────────┘

   He found another dime. Draw the dime.
   How much money does Dan have now? _____

3. Someone made a mistake when they put these number cards in order. Circle a
   number card that you would move so that the number cards will be in order.

   ☐8☐  ☐14☐  ☐18☐  ☐17☐  ☐23☐  ☐29☐  ☐34☐

4. Color the even numbers yellow in Problem 3.

5. Fill in the missing numbers.

   ☐        3        ☐        9        6        ☐
   + 8     + ☐     + 5     + ☐     + ☐     + 0
   ────     ────     ────     ────     ────     ────
   10       10       10       10       10       10

6. Ask exactly 10 people whether they like cats or dogs better.
   Show their choice on this graph.

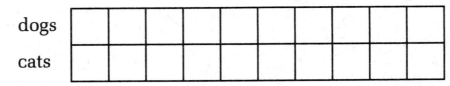

   Which pet did most of the people you asked like better? _____

Name _____

Date _____

1.  There were four books on the table. Patty put three of the books in the closet. Draw a picture and write a number sentence to show how many books are on the table now.

[ ]

Number sentence _____

How many books are on the table now? _____ book

2.  How many more children cut out pink hearts than red hearts?

    _____ children

|       | Hearts |   |   |   |   |   |   |
|-------|--------|---|---|---|---|---|---|
| red   | ♡ | ♡ | ♡ | ♡ |   |   |   |
| pink  | ♡ | ♡ | ♡ | ♡ | ♡ | ♡ |   |

3.  Julie put her pennies in groups of 10.

    How many pennies does she have? _____

    How much money is this? _____

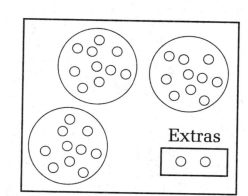

    Extras

4.  Fill in the answers.

    $6 + 5 =$ _____     $9 + 8 =$ _____     $6 + 7 =$ _____

    $4 + 5 =$ _____     $8 + 7 =$ _____     $3 + 4 =$ _____

5.  Tim's receipt at the classroom store looked like this.

    How much money did he spend for the two items? _____

    How many dimes is that? _____

    How many pennies is that? _____

| eggs  |   | 43 | ¢ |
|-------|---|----|---|
| rolls | + | 13 | ¢ |
| Total |   |    | ¢ |

$$\begin{array}{r} 3 \\ + \square \\ \hline 10 \end{array} \qquad \begin{array}{r} 8 \\ + \square \\ \hline 10 \end{array} \qquad \begin{array}{r} \square \\ + 4 \\ \hline 10 \end{array} \qquad \begin{array}{r} 5 \\ + \square \\ \hline 10 \end{array} \qquad \begin{array}{r} \square \\ + 1 \\ \hline 10 \end{array}$$

$$\begin{array}{r} 2 \\ + \square \\ \hline 10 \end{array} \qquad \begin{array}{r} 6 \\ + \square \\ \hline 10 \end{array} \qquad \begin{array}{r} \square \\ + 5 \\ \hline 10 \end{array} \qquad \begin{array}{r} \square \\ + 3 \\ \hline 10 \end{array} \qquad \begin{array}{r} 9 \\ + \square \\ \hline 10 \end{array}$$

$$\begin{array}{r} 7 \\ + \square \\ \hline 10 \end{array} \qquad \begin{array}{r} \square \\ + 1 \\ \hline 10 \end{array} \qquad \begin{array}{r} 5 \\ + \square \\ \hline 10 \end{array} \qquad \begin{array}{r} 4 \\ + \square \\ \hline 10 \end{array} \qquad \begin{array}{r} \square \\ + 8 \\ \hline 10 \end{array}$$

$$\begin{array}{r} 9 \\ + \square \\ \hline 10 \end{array} \qquad \begin{array}{r} \square \\ + 2 \\ \hline 10 \end{array} \qquad \begin{array}{r} 6 \\ + \square \\ \hline 10 \end{array} \qquad \begin{array}{r} \square \\ + 5 \\ \hline 10 \end{array} \qquad \begin{array}{r} \square \\ + 7 \\ \hline 10 \end{array}$$

$$\begin{array}{r} 1 \\ + \square \\ \hline 10 \end{array} \qquad \begin{array}{r} \square \\ + 6 \\ \hline 10 \end{array} \qquad \begin{array}{r} 3 \\ + \square \\ \hline 10 \end{array} \qquad \begin{array}{r} 8 \\ + \square \\ \hline 10 \end{array} \qquad \begin{array}{r} \square \\ + 5 \\ \hline 10 \end{array}$$

core: _____

Name <u> • </u>

Date <u>                            </u>

Day of the Week <u>                        </u>

1. Write the number eighty-six four more times. How many digits are on the line? \_\_\_\_

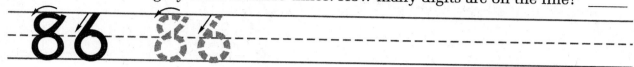

2. Write a story for the number sentence **6 − 2 = 4**.

   _____

   _____

   _____

3. Fill in the missing numbers.

   100, 200, 300, \_\_\_\_ , \_\_\_\_ , \_\_\_\_ , \_\_\_\_ , \_\_\_\_ , \_\_\_\_

   45, 44, 43, \_\_\_\_ , \_\_\_\_ , \_\_\_\_ , \_\_\_\_ , \_\_\_\_ , \_\_\_\_

   5, 10, 15, \_\_\_\_ , \_\_\_\_ , \_\_\_\_ , \_\_\_\_ , \_\_\_\_ , \_\_\_\_

4. Color the congruent shapes blue.

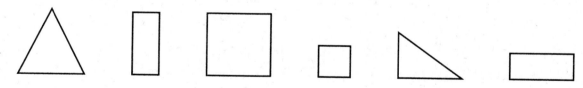

5. Find the total on each receipt.

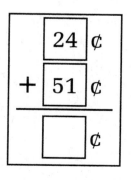
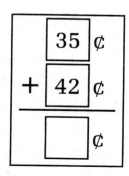
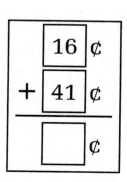

\_\_\_\_ dimes \_\_\_\_ pennies      \_\_\_\_ dimes \_\_\_\_ pennies      \_\_\_\_ dimes \_\_\_\_ pennies

-95Wa

1. Color the first book red.
   Color the sixth book blue.
   Color the third book green.
   Color the seventh book yellow.
   Color the fifth book orange.

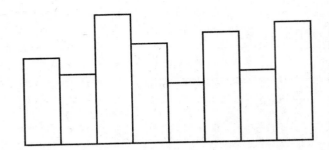

2. Write a story for the number sentence **9 – 1 = 8**.

   _____

   _____

   _____

3. Fill in the missing numbers.

   200, 300, 400, ____ , ____ , ____ , ____ , ____

   26, 27, 28, ____ , ____ , ____ , ____ , ____ , ____

   45, 40, 35, ____ , ____ , ____ , ____ , ____ , ____

4. Color the congruent shapes blue (same size and shape).

5. Find the total on each receipt.

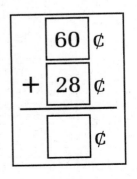 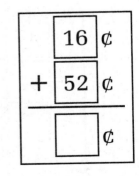 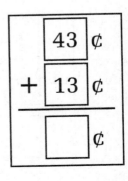

____ dimes ____ pennies     ____ dimes ____ pennies     ____ dimes ____ pennie

Name _____

Name _____

**MASTER 1-96A**

*Math 1*

$$\begin{array}{r} 3 \\ + \;\square \\ \hline 10 \end{array} \qquad \begin{array}{r} 8 \\ + \;\square \\ \hline 10 \end{array} \qquad \begin{array}{r} \square \\ + \;4 \\ \hline 10 \end{array} \qquad \begin{array}{r} 5 \\ + \;\square \\ \hline 10 \end{array} \qquad \begin{array}{r} \square \\ + \;1 \\ \hline 10 \end{array}$$

$$\begin{array}{r} 2 \\ + \;\square \\ \hline 10 \end{array} \qquad \begin{array}{r} 6 \\ + \;\square \\ \hline 10 \end{array} \qquad \begin{array}{r} \square \\ + \;5 \\ \hline 10 \end{array} \qquad \begin{array}{r} \square \\ + \;3 \\ \hline 10 \end{array} \qquad \begin{array}{r} 9 \\ + \;\square \\ \hline 10 \end{array}$$

$$\begin{array}{r} 7 \\ + \;\square \\ \hline 10 \end{array} \qquad \begin{array}{r} \square \\ + \;1 \\ \hline 10 \end{array} \qquad \begin{array}{r} 5 \\ + \;\square \\ \hline 10 \end{array} \qquad \begin{array}{r} 4 \\ + \;\square \\ \hline 10 \end{array} \qquad \begin{array}{r} \square \\ + \;8 \\ \hline 10 \end{array}$$

$$\begin{array}{r} 9 \\ + \;\square \\ \hline 10 \end{array} \qquad \begin{array}{r} \square \\ + \;2 \\ \hline 10 \end{array} \qquad \begin{array}{r} 6 \\ + \;\square \\ \hline 10 \end{array} \qquad \begin{array}{r} \square \\ + \;5 \\ \hline 10 \end{array} \qquad \begin{array}{r} \square \\ + \;7 \\ \hline 10 \end{array}$$

$$\begin{array}{r} 1 \\ + \;\square \\ \hline 10 \end{array} \qquad \begin{array}{r} \square \\ + \;6 \\ \hline 10 \end{array} \qquad \begin{array}{r} 3 \\ + \;\square \\ \hline 10 \end{array} \qquad \begin{array}{r} 8 \\ + \;\square \\ \hline 10 \end{array} \qquad \begin{array}{r} \square \\ + \;5 \\ \hline 10 \end{array}$$

Score: _____

Name ●

Date _____

Day of the Week _____

1. Write the number eighty-seven three more times. How many digits did you use? _____

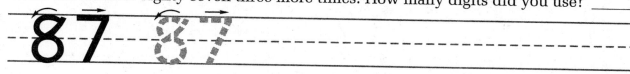

2. Betty has two rolls.
   Draw the rolls.
   She cut the rolls into four equal pieces.
   Show how she cut the rolls.

   How many pieces of roll does she have?

   _____ pieces

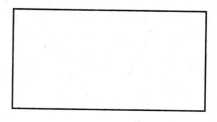

3. Fill in the missing numbers.

   $6 + \boxed{\phantom{0}} = 10$     $3 + \boxed{\phantom{0}} = 10$     $\boxed{\phantom{0}} + 9 = 10$

4. Draw congruent shapes on the geoboards. (Congruent shapes are the same size and shape.)

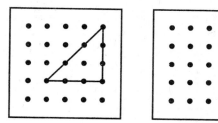

5. Number the clock face.
   Show half past seven on the clock.

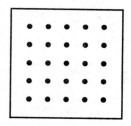

6. Trace the longest line segment using a yellow crayon.
   Trace the shortest line segment using a red crayon.
   Trace the second shortest line segment using a blue crayon.

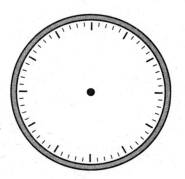

1. Fill in the missing numbers.

   25, 24, 23, _____ , _____ , _____ , _____ , _____ , _____ , _____

   1, 3, 5, _____ , _____ , _____ , _____ , _____ , _____ , _____

2. Justin has three rolls.
   Draw the rolls.
   He cut the rolls into two equal pieces.
   Show how he cut the rolls.

   How many pieces of roll does he have now?

   _____ pieces

   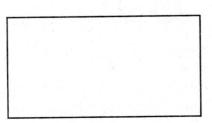

3. Fill in the missing numbers.

   ☐ + 7 = 10        1 + ☐ = 10        ☐ + 2 = 10

4. Draw congruent shapes on the geoboards.
   (Congruent shapes are the same size and shape.)

   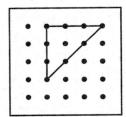  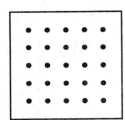  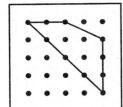  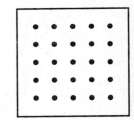

5. Number the clock face.
   Show half past five on the clock.

6. Trace the longest line segment using a yellow crayon.
   Trace the shortest line segment using a red crayon.
   Trace the second shortest line segment using a blue crayon.

   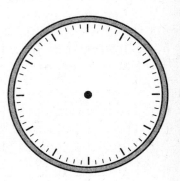

   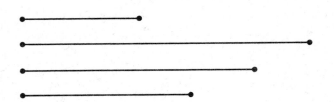

Name _____    **MASTER 1-97**
                                                          *Math 1*

1.  •————————————•    _____ inches

2.  •————————————————————————•    _____ inches

3.  •————————————————•    _____ inches

4.  •
       \
        \
         \
          \
           •    _____ inches

                                              •
                                             /
                                            /
                                           /
                                          /
                                         /
                                        /
                                       /
                                      /
                                     /
                                    /    _____ inches
                                   /
5.  •

Name _____

$$\begin{array}{r} 3 \\ + \boxed{\phantom{0}} \\ \hline 10 \end{array} \quad \begin{array}{r} 8 \\ + \boxed{\phantom{0}} \\ \hline 10 \end{array} \quad \begin{array}{r} \boxed{\phantom{0}} \\ + 4 \\ \hline 10 \end{array} \quad \begin{array}{r} 5 \\ + \boxed{\phantom{0}} \\ \hline 10 \end{array} \quad \begin{array}{r} \boxed{\phantom{0}} \\ + 1 \\ \hline 10 \end{array}$$

$$\begin{array}{r} 2 \\ + \boxed{\phantom{0}} \\ \hline 10 \end{array} \quad \begin{array}{r} 6 \\ + \boxed{\phantom{0}} \\ \hline 10 \end{array} \quad \begin{array}{r} \boxed{\phantom{0}} \\ + 5 \\ \hline 10 \end{array} \quad \begin{array}{r} \boxed{\phantom{0}} \\ + 3 \\ \hline 10 \end{array} \quad \begin{array}{r} 9 \\ + \boxed{\phantom{0}} \\ \hline 10 \end{array}$$

$$\begin{array}{r} 7 \\ + \boxed{\phantom{0}} \\ \hline 10 \end{array} \quad \begin{array}{r} \boxed{\phantom{0}} \\ + 1 \\ \hline 10 \end{array} \quad \begin{array}{r} 5 \\ + \boxed{\phantom{0}} \\ \hline 10 \end{array} \quad \begin{array}{r} 4 \\ + \boxed{\phantom{0}} \\ \hline 10 \end{array} \quad \begin{array}{r} \boxed{\phantom{0}} \\ + 8 \\ \hline 10 \end{array}$$

$$\begin{array}{r} 9 \\ + \boxed{\phantom{0}} \\ \hline 10 \end{array} \quad \begin{array}{r} \boxed{\phantom{0}} \\ + 2 \\ \hline 10 \end{array} \quad \begin{array}{r} 6 \\ + \boxed{\phantom{0}} \\ \hline 10 \end{array} \quad \begin{array}{r} \boxed{\phantom{0}} \\ + 5 \\ \hline 10 \end{array} \quad \begin{array}{r} \boxed{\phantom{0}} \\ + 7 \\ \hline 10 \end{array}$$

$$\begin{array}{r} 1 \\ + \boxed{\phantom{0}} \\ \hline 10 \end{array} \quad \begin{array}{r} \boxed{\phantom{0}} \\ + 6 \\ \hline 10 \end{array} \quad \begin{array}{r} 3 \\ + \boxed{\phantom{0}} \\ \hline 10 \end{array} \quad \begin{array}{r} 8 \\ + \boxed{\phantom{0}} \\ \hline 10 \end{array} \quad \begin{array}{r} \boxed{\phantom{0}} \\ + 5 \\ \hline 10 \end{array}$$

Score: _____

Name _____ •
    (Draw a 4-inch line segment.)

Date _____

Day of the Week _____

1. Write the number eighty-eight three more times. How many digits did you use? _____

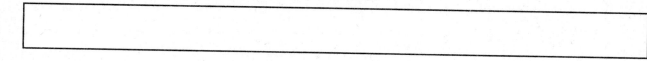

2. Gary had two number cards with the numbers **13** and **25**. Tom gave him three more number cards with the numbers **42**, **16**, and **21**. Draw a picture and write a number sentence to show how many number cards Gary has now.

   [ ]

   Number sentence _____

   How many number cards does Gary have now? _____ number cards

3. Put the number cards in Problem 2 in order from least to greatest.  [ ] [ ] [ ] [ ] [ ]

4. Draw a congruent shape on the geoboard.

   Trace each side using a different color.

   How many sides does this shape have?

   _____ sides

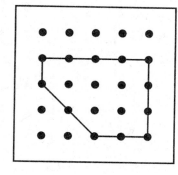 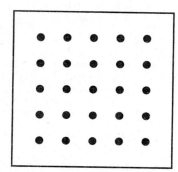

5. Fill in the missing numbers.

   $\boxed{\phantom{0}} + 2 = 3$     $1 + \boxed{\phantom{0}} = 10$     $\boxed{\phantom{0}} + 4 = 4$

6. Add 10 to each number.

   | 41 | | 87 | | 19 |
   |----|----|----|----|----|
   | | | | | |

   $\begin{array}{r} 62¢ \\ + 10¢ \\ \hline \end{array}$     $\begin{array}{r} 43¢ \\ + 10¢ \\ \hline \end{array}$     $\begin{array}{r} 17¢ \\ + 10¢ \\ \hline \end{array}$

1. Circle the one that is different.

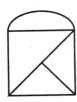   

2. Charlie had four number cards with the numbers **23**, **16**, **35**, and **19**. David gave him one more number card with the number **27**. Draw a picture and write a number sentence to show how many number cards Charlie has now.

Number sentence _____

How many number cards does Charlie have now? _____ number cards

3. Put the number cards in Problem 2 in order from least to greatest.

☐ ☐ ☐ ☐ ☐

4. Draw a congruent shape on the geoboard.

Trace each side using a different color.

How many sides does this shape have?

_____ sides

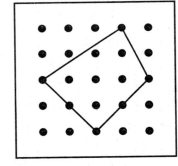 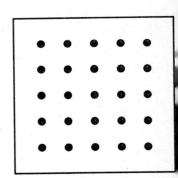

5. Fill in the missing numbers.

☐ + 0 = 5     7 + ☐ = 10     ☐ + 1 = 7

6. Add 10 to each number.

| 39 | | 84 | | 11 |

$$54¢ \atop + 10¢$$     $$23¢ \atop + 10¢$$     $$13¢ \atop + 10¢$$

|        |        |        |         |        |
|--------|--------|--------|---------|--------|
| 8 − 2  | 5 − 2  | 2 − 2  | 10 − 2  | 6 − 2  |
| 7 − 2  | 3 − 2  | 11 − 2 | 9 − 2   | 4 − 2  |
| 11 − 2 | 2 − 2  | 7 − 2  | 4 − 2   | 10 − 2 |
| 6 − 2  | 8 − 2  | 3 − 2  | 9 − 2   | 5 − 2  |
| 8 − 2  | 7 − 2  | 5 − 2  | 11 − 2  | 4 − 2  |

core: _____

Name _____

(Draw a 4-inch line segment.)

Date _____

Day of the Week _____

1. Write the number eighty-nine two more times. How many digits did you use? _____

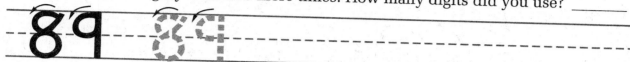

2. Danielle made six bookmarks. She gave two to Michael. Draw a picture and write a number sentence to show how many bookmarks she has now.

[blank box]

Number sentence_____     _____ bookmarks

3. The children in Miss Walker's class made the following shapes on their geoboards. They turned their geoboards in different directions.

Circle the shape that is not congruent to the other five shapes.

4. Write the answers.

$9 - 2 =$ ____          $6 - 2 =$ ____          $8 - 2 =$ ____

5. Show half past ten on the clock.

6. Bob put the linking cubes in trains of 10. How many linking cubes does he have?

_____ linking cubes

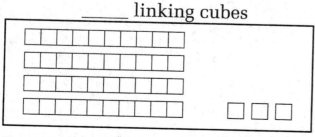

7. How many tally marks are in the rectangle? _____

98Wa

Name _____

1. Fill in the missing numbers.

   5, 10, 15, _____ , _____ , _____ , _____ , _____ , _____ , _____

   35, 36, 37, _____ , _____ , _____ , _____ , _____ , _____ , _____

2. Craig made nine bookmarks. He gave two bookmarks to Stephanie. Draw a picture and write a number sentence to show how many bookmarks he has now.

   [          ]

   Number sentence _____        _____ bookmarks

3. The children in Mr. Hodge's class made the following shapes on their geoboards. They turned their geoboards in different directions.

   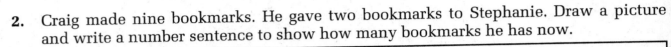
   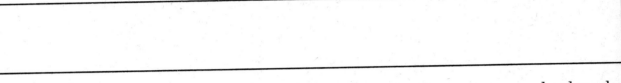

   Circle the shape that is not congruent to the other five.

4. Write the answers.

   7 – 2 = _____        5 – 2 = _____        8 – 2 = _____

5. Show half past three on the clock.

6. Jermaine put the linking cubes in trains of 10. How many linking cubes does he have?

   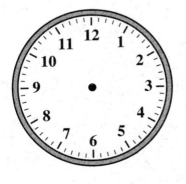

   _____ linking cubes

   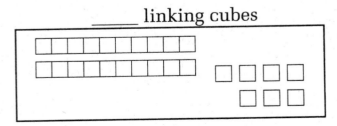

7. How many tally marks are in the rectangle? _____

   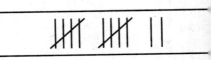

Name _____

$$\begin{array}{r} 8 \\ -\ 2 \\ \hline \end{array} \qquad \begin{array}{r} 5 \\ -\ 2 \\ \hline \end{array} \qquad \begin{array}{r} 2 \\ -\ 2 \\ \hline \end{array} \qquad \begin{array}{r} 10 \\ -\ 2 \\ \hline \end{array} \qquad \begin{array}{r} 6 \\ -\ 2 \\ \hline \end{array}$$

$$\begin{array}{r} 7 \\ -\ 2 \\ \hline \end{array} \qquad \begin{array}{r} 3 \\ -\ 2 \\ \hline \end{array} \qquad \begin{array}{r} 11 \\ -\ 2 \\ \hline \end{array} \qquad \begin{array}{r} 9 \\ -\ 2 \\ \hline \end{array} \qquad \begin{array}{r} 4 \\ -\ 2 \\ \hline \end{array}$$

$$\begin{array}{r} 11 \\ -\ 2 \\ \hline \end{array} \qquad \begin{array}{r} 2 \\ -\ 2 \\ \hline \end{array} \qquad \begin{array}{r} 7 \\ -\ 2 \\ \hline \end{array} \qquad \begin{array}{r} 4 \\ -\ 2 \\ \hline \end{array} \qquad \begin{array}{r} 10 \\ -\ 2 \\ \hline \end{array}$$

$$\begin{array}{r} 6 \\ -\ 2 \\ \hline \end{array} \qquad \begin{array}{r} 8 \\ -\ 2 \\ \hline \end{array} \qquad \begin{array}{r} 3 \\ -\ 2 \\ \hline \end{array} \qquad \begin{array}{r} 9 \\ -\ 2 \\ \hline \end{array} \qquad \begin{array}{r} 5 \\ -\ 2 \\ \hline \end{array}$$

$$\begin{array}{r} 8 \\ -\ 2 \\ \hline \end{array} \qquad \begin{array}{r} 7 \\ -\ 2 \\ \hline \end{array} \qquad \begin{array}{r} 5 \\ -\ 2 \\ \hline \end{array} \qquad \begin{array}{r} 11 \\ -\ 2 \\ \hline \end{array} \qquad \begin{array}{r} 4 \\ -\ 2 \\ \hline \end{array}$$

Score: _____

Name _____ •
(Draw a 4-inch line segment.)

Date _____

Day of the Week _____

1. Write the number ninety three more times. How many digits did you use? _____

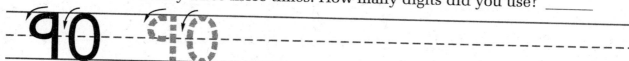

2. Write a number word with one vowel and two consonants. _____
   Circle the vowel with a red crayon.
   Circle the consonants with a green crayon.

   How many letters did you write? _____

3. Circle groups of two nickels. How much money is this? _____

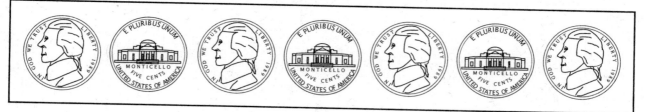

4. Measure these line segments using inches.

   _____ inches

   _____ inches

5. Put these numbers in order from least to greatest.

   | 24 | 32 | 16 | 27 |
   |----|----|----|----|

   ☐ ☐ ☐ ☐
   least        greatest

6. Choose 5 numbers on the hundred number chart. Add 10 to each number.

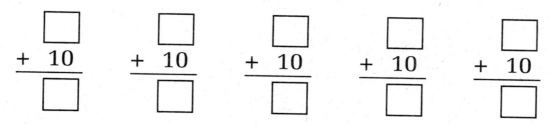

   ☐        ☐        ☐        ☐        ☐
   + 10     + 10     + 10     + 10     + 10
   ☐        ☐        ☐        ☐        ☐

1-99Wa

1. Fill in the missing numbers.

| | | | 44 | 46 | | | 50 |
|---|---|---|---|---|---|---|---|
| 51 | | | 55 | | | | |

2. Write a number word with two vowels and two consonants. _____
   Circle the vowels with a red crayon.
   Circle the consonants with a green crayon.

   How many letters did you write? _____

3. Circle groups of two nickels. How much money is this? _____

4. Write the answers.

$$
\begin{array}{cccccccc}
4 & \quad 5 & \quad 8 & \quad 1 & \quad 3 & \quad 6 & \quad 0 \\
+\,6 & \quad +\,2 & \quad +\,9 & \quad +\,6 & \quad +\,7 & \quad +\,5 & \quad +\,8 \\
\end{array}
$$

5. Put these numbers in order from least to greatest.

   | 42 | 25 | 36 | 12 |
   |---|---|---|---|

   ▢ ▢ ▢ ▢
   least        greatest

6. Add 10 to each number.

   | 83 | | 16 | | 39 |
   |---|---|---|---|---|
   | | | | | |

   $$
   \begin{array}{ccc}
   19\cent & \quad 6\cent & \quad 25\cent \\
   +\,10\cent & \quad +\,10\cent & \quad +\,10\cent \\
   \end{array}
   $$

Name •
  (Draw a line segment for your name.)

Date _____

Day of the Week _____

1. Lucy drew ten pictures. She sent two pictures to her grandmother. Draw the pictures and write a number sentence to show how many pictures Lucy has left.

Number sentence _____

How many pictures does Lucy have left? _____ pictures

2. Color the congruent shapes red.

3. Divide the squares into fourths in two different ways. Color one fourth of each square.

4. Color the pennies brown. How much money is this? _____

5. Fill in the missing numbers.

   35, 34, 33, ____ , ____ , ____ , ____ , ____ , ____

   2, 4, 6, ____ , ____ , ____ , ____ , ____ , ____ , ____

   5, 10, 15, ____ , ____ , ____ , ____ , ____ , ____ , ____

$$\begin{array}{r} 8 \\ -\ 2 \\ \hline \end{array} \qquad \begin{array}{r} 5 \\ -\ 2 \\ \hline \end{array} \qquad \begin{array}{r} 2 \\ -\ 2 \\ \hline \end{array} \qquad \begin{array}{r} 10 \\ -\ 2 \\ \hline \end{array} \qquad \begin{array}{r} 6 \\ -\ 2 \\ \hline \end{array}$$

$$\begin{array}{r} 7 \\ -\ 2 \\ \hline \end{array} \qquad \begin{array}{r} 3 \\ -\ 2 \\ \hline \end{array} \qquad \begin{array}{r} 11 \\ -\ 2 \\ \hline \end{array} \qquad \begin{array}{r} 9 \\ -\ 2 \\ \hline \end{array} \qquad \begin{array}{r} 4 \\ -\ 2 \\ \hline \end{array}$$

$$\begin{array}{r} 11 \\ -\ 2 \\ \hline \end{array} \qquad \begin{array}{r} 2 \\ -\ 2 \\ \hline \end{array} \qquad \begin{array}{r} 7 \\ -\ 2 \\ \hline \end{array} \qquad \begin{array}{r} 4 \\ -\ 2 \\ \hline \end{array} \qquad \begin{array}{r} 10 \\ -\ 2 \\ \hline \end{array}$$

$$\begin{array}{r} 6 \\ -\ 2 \\ \hline \end{array} \qquad \begin{array}{r} 8 \\ -\ 2 \\ \hline \end{array} \qquad \begin{array}{r} 3 \\ -\ 2 \\ \hline \end{array} \qquad \begin{array}{r} 9 \\ -\ 2 \\ \hline \end{array} \qquad \begin{array}{r} 5 \\ -\ 2 \\ \hline \end{array}$$

$$\begin{array}{r} 8 \\ -\ 2 \\ \hline \end{array} \qquad \begin{array}{r} 7 \\ -\ 2 \\ \hline \end{array} \qquad \begin{array}{r} 5 \\ -\ 2 \\ \hline \end{array} \qquad \begin{array}{r} 11 \\ -\ 2 \\ \hline \end{array} \qquad \begin{array}{r} 4 \\ -\ 2 \\ \hline \end{array}$$

Score: _____

Name _____ •
    (Draw a 4-inch line segment.)

Date _____

Day of the Week _____

**1.** Write the number ninety-one five more times. How many digits are on the line? _____

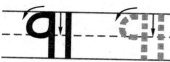

- - - - - - - - - - - - - - - - - - - - - - - - - - - - - - - - - - - - - - - - -

**2.** Write a story for the number sentence **6 + 2 = 8.**

_____

_____

_____

**3.** Color each congruent shape on the calendar using the same color. Use red, yellow, and blue.

**March**

| Sunday | Monday | Tuesday | Wednesday | Thursday | Friday | Saturday |
|--------|--------|---------|-----------|----------|--------|----------|
| 1 | 2 | 3 | 4 | 5 | 6 | 7 |
| 8 | 9 | 10 | 11 | 12 | 13 | 14 |
| 15 | 16 | 17 | | | | |

**4.** What was the date of the first Monday in March?

_____

**5.** Someone put the number cards in the box in order. One card is missing. Cross out the number cards you cannot use. Circle the number card that belongs in the space with the **A**.

| 16 | 23 | 29 | A | 36 |    | 42 | 27 | 34 | 38 |

**6.** Color the pennies brown. Circle groups of 2 nickels. How much money is this? _____

1. Circle the two shapes that are exactly the same.

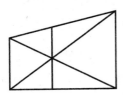 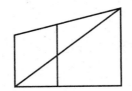 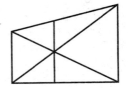 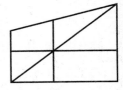

2. Write a story for the number sentence **4 + 3 = 7**.

_____

_____

_____

3. Color each congruent shape on the calendar using the same color. Use red, yellow, and blue.

4. What was the date of the first Wednesday in January?

_____

**January**

| Sunday | Monday | Tuesday | Wednesday | Thursday | Friday | Saturday |
|--------|--------|---------|-----------|----------|--------|----------|
|  | 1 | 2 | 3 | 4 | 5 | 6 |
| 7 | 8 | 9 | 10 | 11 | 12 | 13 |
| 14 | 15 |  |  |  |  |  |

5. Someone put the number cards in the box in order. One card is missing. Cross out the number cards you cannot use. Circle the number card that belongs in the space with the **B**.

| 14 | 27 | B | 35 | 38 |   | 41 | 37 | 26 | 32 |

6. Color the pennies brown. Circle groups of 2 nickels. How much money is this? _____

$$\begin{array}{r} 3 \\ -\ 2 \\ \hline \end{array} \qquad \begin{array}{r} 6 \\ -\ 1 \\ \hline \end{array} \qquad \begin{array}{r} 5 \\ -\ 0 \\ \hline \end{array} \qquad \begin{array}{r} 7 \\ -\ 2 \\ \hline \end{array} \qquad \begin{array}{r} 8 \\ -\ 4 \\ \hline \end{array}$$

$$\begin{array}{r} 6 \\ -\ 6 \\ \hline \end{array} \qquad \begin{array}{r} 8 \\ -\ 2 \\ \hline \end{array} \qquad \begin{array}{r} 9 \\ -\ 1 \\ \hline \end{array} \qquad \begin{array}{r} 14 \\ -\ 7 \\ \hline \end{array} \qquad \begin{array}{r} 9 \\ -\ 2 \\ \hline \end{array}$$

$$\begin{array}{r} 16 \\ -\ 8 \\ \hline \end{array} \qquad \begin{array}{r} 3 \\ -\ 0 \\ \hline \end{array} \qquad \begin{array}{r} 4 \\ -\ 2 \\ \hline \end{array} \qquad \begin{array}{r} 5 \\ -\ 1 \\ \hline \end{array} \qquad \begin{array}{r} 11 \\ -\ 2 \\ \hline \end{array}$$

$$\begin{array}{r} 8 \\ -\ 0 \\ \hline \end{array} \qquad \begin{array}{r} 12 \\ -\ 6 \\ \hline \end{array} \qquad \begin{array}{r} 5 \\ -\ 2 \\ \hline \end{array} \qquad \begin{array}{r} 3 \\ -\ 1 \\ \hline \end{array} \qquad \begin{array}{r} 6 \\ -\ 3 \\ \hline \end{array}$$

$$\begin{array}{r} 10 \\ -\ 2 \\ \hline \end{array} \qquad \begin{array}{r} 18 \\ -\ 9 \\ \hline \end{array} \qquad \begin{array}{r} 7 \\ -\ 1 \\ \hline \end{array} \qquad \begin{array}{r} 6 \\ -\ 2 \\ \hline \end{array} \qquad \begin{array}{r} 7 \\ -\ 7 \\ \hline \end{array}$$

core: _____

Name _____ •
(Draw a 4-inch line segment.)

Date _____

Day of the Week _____

1. Write the number ninety-two four more times. How many digits did you use? _____

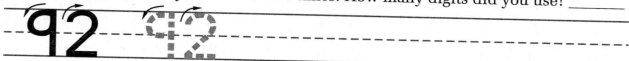

2. Mark had seven pet frogs. He gave two frogs to Christopher. What type of story is this?

   some, some more          some, some went away

   Draw a picture and write a number sentence to show how many frogs Mark has now.

   _____

   Number sentence _____ Answer _____ frogs

3. Color the pennies brown.

   How much money is this?

   _____

4. Circle the shape that is divided into fourths. Color one fourth red. Put an X below the shape divided into halves. Color one half blue.

5. Show half past eleven on the clock.

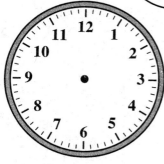

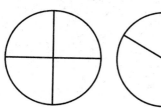

6. Brendan bought milk for 43¢ and cereal for 26¢ at the classroom store. Show how he filled out the receipt.

Name _____

1. Circle the number that is between 25 and 35.

   23          27          36          42

2. Roxanne's dog had six puppies. She gave two puppies to Teresa. What type of story is this?

   some, some more          some, some went away

   Draw a picture and write a number sentence to show how many puppies Roxanne has now.

   [                                              ]

   Number sentence _____   Answer _____ puppies

3. Color the pennies brown.

   How much money is this?

   _____

4. Circle the shape that is divided into fourths. Color one fourth red. Put an X below the shape divided into halves. Color one half blue.

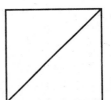 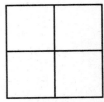

5. Show half past two on the clock.

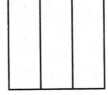

6. Rondo bought bread for 31¢ and jelly for 28¢ at the classroom store. Show how he filled out the receipt.

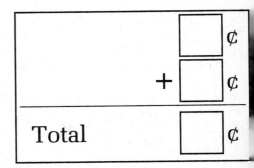

$$\begin{array}{r} 3 \\ -\ 2 \\ \hline \end{array} \qquad \begin{array}{r} 6 \\ -\ 1 \\ \hline \end{array} \qquad \begin{array}{r} 5 \\ -\ 0 \\ \hline \end{array} \qquad \begin{array}{r} 7 \\ -\ 2 \\ \hline \end{array} \qquad \begin{array}{r} 8 \\ -\ 4 \\ \hline \end{array}$$

$$\begin{array}{r} 6 \\ -\ 6 \\ \hline \end{array} \qquad \begin{array}{r} 8 \\ -\ 2 \\ \hline \end{array} \qquad \begin{array}{r} 9 \\ -\ 1 \\ \hline \end{array} \qquad \begin{array}{r} 14 \\ -\ 7 \\ \hline \end{array} \qquad \begin{array}{r} 9 \\ -\ 2 \\ \hline \end{array}$$

$$\begin{array}{r} 16 \\ -\ 8 \\ \hline \end{array} \qquad \begin{array}{r} 3 \\ -\ 0 \\ \hline \end{array} \qquad \begin{array}{r} 4 \\ -\ 2 \\ \hline \end{array} \qquad \begin{array}{r} 5 \\ -\ 1 \\ \hline \end{array} \qquad \begin{array}{r} 11 \\ -\ 2 \\ \hline \end{array}$$

$$\begin{array}{r} 8 \\ -\ 0 \\ \hline \end{array} \qquad \begin{array}{r} 12 \\ -\ 6 \\ \hline \end{array} \qquad \begin{array}{r} 5 \\ -\ 2 \\ \hline \end{array} \qquad \begin{array}{r} 3 \\ -\ 1 \\ \hline \end{array} \qquad \begin{array}{r} 6 \\ -\ 3 \\ \hline \end{array}$$

$$\begin{array}{r} 10 \\ -\ 2 \\ \hline \end{array} \qquad \begin{array}{r} 18 \\ -\ 9 \\ \hline \end{array} \qquad \begin{array}{r} 7 \\ -\ 1 \\ \hline \end{array} \qquad \begin{array}{r} 6 \\ -\ 2 \\ \hline \end{array} \qquad \begin{array}{r} 7 \\ -\ 7 \\ \hline \end{array}$$

Score: _____

Name  •
   (Draw a 3-inch line segment.)

Date  _____

Day of the Week  _____

1. Write the number ninety-three two more times. How many digits did you use? _____

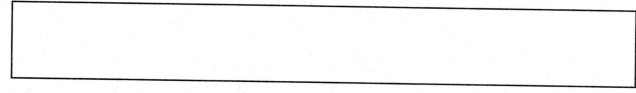

2. On Tuesday, Cerina counted eight fish in the fish tank. Mrs. O' Connor put two more fish in the tank on Wednesday. What type of story is this?

         some, some more           some, some went away

Draw a picture and write a number sentence to show how many fish are in the tank now.

Number sentence _____    Answer _____ fish

3. There are 8 candies in the bag. Show how Brian and Michael will share the candies.

         candies              Brian              Michael

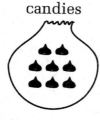 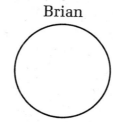 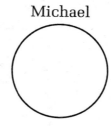

How many candies will each boy have? _____ candies

4. Count by 10's from 4.

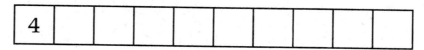

5. Write six different examples with a sum of 10.

Date _____

1. Fill in the missing numbers.

   10, 12, 14, ____ , ____ , ____

   34, 33, 32, ____ , ____ , ____ , ____ , ____

   100, 200, 300, ____ , ____ , ____ , ____ , ____

2. On Thursday, Roger counted seven stickers on the chart. Ms. Treat put two more stickers on the chart on Friday. What type of story is this?

   some, some more          some, some went away

   Draw a picture and write a number sentence to show how many stickers are on the chart now.

   

   Number sentence _____     Answer _____ stickers

3. There are 10 candies in the bag. Show how Rosa and Pam will share the candies.

   candies                Rosa                Pam

   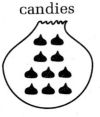   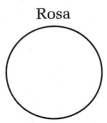   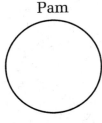

   How many candies will each girl have? _____ candies

4. Count by 10's from 3.     | 3 | | | | | | | | | |

5. Fill in the missing numbers.

   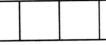

   $$\begin{array}{r} \square \\ +\ 4 \\ \hline 10 \end{array} \qquad \begin{array}{r} 3 \\ +\ \square \\ \hline 10 \end{array} \qquad \begin{array}{r} \square \\ +\ 8 \\ \hline 10 \end{array} \qquad \begin{array}{r} \square \\ +\ 1 \\ \hline 10 \end{array} \qquad \begin{array}{r} 5 \\ +\ \square \\ \hline 10 \end{array} \qquad \begin{array}{r} 7 \\ +\ \square \\ \hline 10 \end{array}$$

   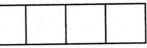

$$\begin{array}{r} 3 \\ -\ 2 \\ \hline \end{array} \qquad \begin{array}{r} 6 \\ -\ 1 \\ \hline \end{array} \qquad \begin{array}{r} 5 \\ -\ 0 \\ \hline \end{array} \qquad \begin{array}{r} 7 \\ -\ 2 \\ \hline \end{array} \qquad \begin{array}{r} 8 \\ -\ 4 \\ \hline \end{array}$$

$$\begin{array}{r} 6 \\ -\ 6 \\ \hline \end{array} \qquad \begin{array}{r} 8 \\ -\ 2 \\ \hline \end{array} \qquad \begin{array}{r} 9 \\ -\ 1 \\ \hline \end{array} \qquad \begin{array}{r} 14 \\ -\ 7 \\ \hline \end{array} \qquad \begin{array}{r} 9 \\ -\ 2 \\ \hline \end{array}$$

$$\begin{array}{r} 16 \\ -\ 8 \\ \hline \end{array} \qquad \begin{array}{r} 3 \\ -\ 0 \\ \hline \end{array} \qquad \begin{array}{r} 4 \\ -\ 2 \\ \hline \end{array} \qquad \begin{array}{r} 5 \\ -\ 1 \\ \hline \end{array} \qquad \begin{array}{r} 11 \\ -\ 2 \\ \hline \end{array}$$

$$\begin{array}{r} 8 \\ -\ 0 \\ \hline \end{array} \qquad \begin{array}{r} 12 \\ -\ 6 \\ \hline \end{array} \qquad \begin{array}{r} 5 \\ -\ 2 \\ \hline \end{array} \qquad \begin{array}{r} 3 \\ -\ 1 \\ \hline \end{array} \qquad \begin{array}{r} 6 \\ -\ 3 \\ \hline \end{array}$$

$$\begin{array}{r} 10 \\ -\ 2 \\ \hline \end{array} \qquad \begin{array}{r} 18 \\ -\ 9 \\ \hline \end{array} \qquad \begin{array}{r} 7 \\ -\ 1 \\ \hline \end{array} \qquad \begin{array}{r} 6 \\ -\ 2 \\ \hline \end{array} \qquad \begin{array}{r} 7 \\ -\ 7 \\ \hline \end{array}$$

Score: _____

Name •
   (Draw a 3-inch line segment.)

Date _____

Day of the Week _____

1.  Write the number ninety-four three more times. How many digits did you use? _____

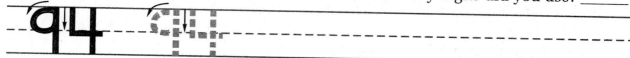

2.  Lorena has 3 dimes and 2 pennies. How much money is that? _____

   Brandy has 2 dimes and 5 pennies. How much money is that? _____

   The girls put their money together.

   How many dimes do they have? _____ dimes

   How many pennies do they have? _____ pennies

   How much money is that? _____

3.  The children in Mrs. Duchesne's class chose their favorite donuts.
    Six children chose chocolate donuts.
    Nine children chose jelly donuts.
    Seven children chose cinnamon donuts.

    Fill in the graph to show how many
    children chose each type of donut.

    What was the favorite donut? _____

    How many more children chose jelly than chose chocolate? _____

Favorite Donuts

chocolate

jelly

cinnamon

4.  Draw a dozen eggs. Color a half dozen brown.

   How many eggs did you color? _____

5.  Color the penny brown. How much money is this? _____

6.  Write the answers.

$9 - 2 =$ _____      $6 - 2 =$ _____      $8 - 2 =$ _____

1. Fill in the missing numbers.

| | | | 64 | | | | 69 | |
|---|---|---|---|---|---|---|---|---|
| | 72 | | | 76 | | | | 80 |

2. Scott has 4 dimes and 1 penny. How much money is that? _____

   Tom has 4 dimes and 5 pennies. How much money is that? _____

   The boys put their money together.

   How many dimes do they have? _____ dimes

   How many pennies do they have? _____ pennies

   How much money is that? _____

3. The children in Mrs. Colwell's class chose their favorite donuts.
   Eight children chose chocolate donuts.
   Five children chose jelly donuts.
   Six children chose cinnamon donuts.

   Fill in the graph to show how many
   children chose each type of donut.

   What was the favorite donut? _____

   How many more children chose chocolate than chose jelly? _____

   Favorite Donuts

   chocolate

   jelly

   cinnamon

4. Draw a dozen apples. Color a half dozen red.

   How many apples did you color? _____

5. Color the penny brown. How much money is this? _____

6. Write the answers.

   $7 - 2 =$ ____      $4 - 2 =$ ____      $9 - 2 =$ ____

Name •
(Draw a line segment for your name.)

Date _____

Day of the Week _____

1. Bonnie had 26¢. Show this using the fewest number of dimes and pennies. Color the pennies brown.

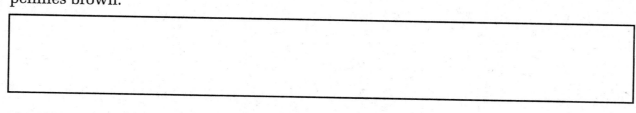

   She found another dime. Draw the dime.

   How much money does Bonnie have now? _____

2. Put the number cards in the box in order from least to greatest.

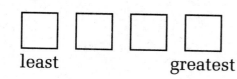

   | 31 | 16 | 47 | 25 |

   ☐ ☐ ☐ ☐
   least        greatest

3. Circle the even numbers.

   1    2    3    4    5    6    7    8    9    10

4. Find the answers.

$$\begin{array}{ccccccc}
5 & 6 & 1 & 7 & 6 & 3 & 5 \\
+\,2 & +\,5 & +\,8 & +\,3 & -\,1 & -\,3 & -\,0 \\
\hline
\end{array}$$

5. Show half past seven on the clock.

6. Add 10 to each number.

   | 29 |     | 18 |        34¢        22¢
   |    |     |    |      + 10¢      + 10¢

-105Aa

| 10 | 10 | 10 | 10 | 10 |
|---|---|---|---|---|
| − 8 | − 4 | − 1 | − 7 | − 3 |

| 10 | 10 | 10 | 10 | 10 |
|---|---|---|---|---|
| − 5 | − 2 | − 9 | − 6 | − 0 |

| 10 | 10 | 10 | 10 | 10 |
|---|---|---|---|---|
| − 10 | − 5 | − 9 | − 6 | − 2 |

| 10 | 10 | 10 | 10 | 10 |
|---|---|---|---|---|
| − 3 | − 7 | − 1 | − 4 | − 8 |

| 10 | 10 | 10 | 10 | 10 |
|---|---|---|---|---|
| − 10 | − 0 | − 6 | − 4 | − 8 |

Score: _____

Name _____
(Draw a 4-inch line segment.)

Date _____

Day of the Week _____

1. Write the number ninety-five four more times. How many digits did you use? _____

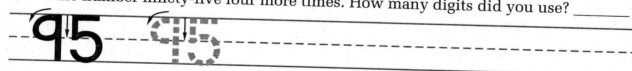

2. James and his brother made a dozen cupcakes.

   Draw the cupcakes.

   They put green frosting on a half dozen.

   Use a green crayon to show that.

   How many cupcakes have green frosting? _____

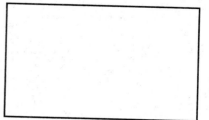

3. Harry and his brother and sister will share the cupcakes with the green frosting.

   How many children will share the cupcakes? _____

   Draw a plate for each child.

   Show how the children will share the cupcakes with the green frosting.

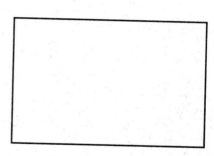

4. Jennifer put the linking cubes in trains of 10.

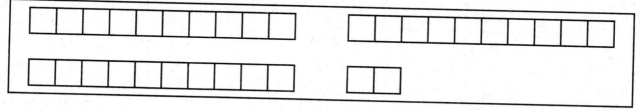

   How many linking cubes does she have? _____ linking cubes

5. Find the answers.

$$\begin{array}{cccccccc} \square & & 3 & & \square & & 5 & \\ +\ 8 & + & \square & + & 4 & + & \square & \\ \hline 10 & & 10 & & 10 & & 10 & \end{array}$$

$$\begin{array}{cccc} 10 & 10 & 10 & 10 \\ -\ 3 & -\ 1 & -\ 6 & -\ 2 \\ \hline \end{array}$$

-105Wa

1. Circle the two designs that are exactly the same.

2. Vickie and her sister boiled a dozen eggs to make hard-boiled eggs.

   Draw the eggs.

   They dyed a half dozen red.

   Use a red crayon to show that.

   How many eggs are red? _____

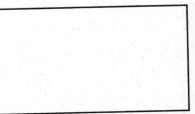

3. Vickie and her sister will share the red eggs.

   How many children will share the red eggs? _____

   Draw a plate for each child.

   Show how the children will share the red eggs.

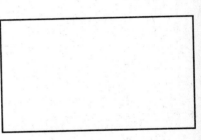

4. Walter put the linking cubes in trains of 10.

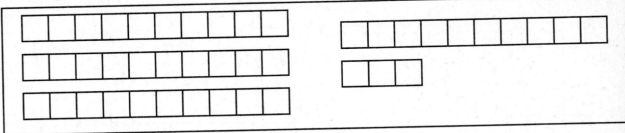

   How many linking cubes does he have? _____ linking cubes

5. Find the answers.

$$
\begin{array}{cccccccc}
2 & & \square & & 6 & & \square \\
+\ \square & & +\ 7 & & +\ \square & & +\ 5 \\
\hline
10 & & 10 & & 10 & & 10
\end{array}
\qquad
\begin{array}{cccc}
10 & 10 & 10 & 10 \\
-\ 9 & -\ 7 & -\ 4 & -\ 8 \\
\end{array}
$$

| 10 | 10 | 10 | 10 | 10 |
|---|---|---|---|---|
| − 8 | − 4 | − 1 | − 7 | − 3 |

| 10 | 10 | 10 | 10 | 10 |
|---|---|---|---|---|
| − 5 | − 2 | − 9 | − 6 | − 0 |

| 10 | 10 | 10 | 10 | 10 |
|---|---|---|---|---|
| − 10 | − 5 | − 9 | − 6 | − 2 |

| 10 | 10 | 10 | 10 | 10 |
|---|---|---|---|---|
| − 3 | − 7 | − 1 | − 4 | − 8 |

| 10 | 10 | 10 | 10 | 10 |
|---|---|---|---|---|
| − 10 | − 0 | − 6 | − 4 | − 8 |

Score: _____

Name •
(Draw a 3-inch line segment.)

Date _____

Day of the Week _____

1.  Write the number ninety-six three more times. How many digits did you use? _____

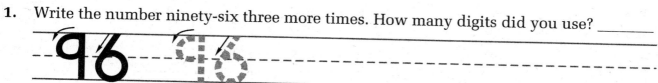

2.  Glenna had a half dozen pencils. She gave two pencils to Nancy. Draw a picture and write a number sentence to show what happened.

    [ ]

    What type of story is this?    some, some more    some, some went away

    Number sentence _____

    How many pencils does Glenna have now? _____ pencils

3.  Circle the geoboard shape that is not congruent to the others.

    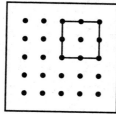 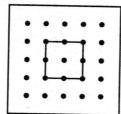 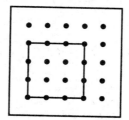 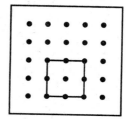

4.  Find the answers.

    $10 - 3 =$ ____        $10 - 6 =$ ____        $10 - 2 =$ ____

5.  Mark has 6 stickers. Show how he will share the stickers with his friend Renee.

    | Mark | Renee |
    |------|-------|
    |      |       |

6.  Use your ruler to measure something in the classroom that is about 1 foot long.

    What did you measure? _____

1-106Wa

1. Finish the number patterns.

   5, 10, 15, _____ , _____ , _____ , _____ , _____

   15, 13, 11, _____ , _____ , _____ , _____ , _____

2. Carol had a half dozen stuffed animals. She gave one stuffed animal to her younger brother. Draw a picture and write a number sentence to show what happened.

   Number sentence _____

   How many stuffed animals does Carol have now? _____ stuffed animals

3. Circle the geoboard shape that is not congruent to the others.

   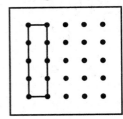 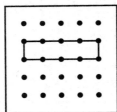 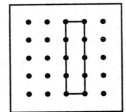 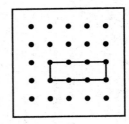

4. Find the answers.

   10 − 7 = _____     10 − 4 = _____     10 − 8 = _____

5. Jessica has 8 toy cars. Show how she will share the cars with her friend Joel.

   Jessica                                    Joel

6. Use your ruler to measure something at home that is about 1 foot long.

   What did you measure? _____

$$\begin{array}{r} 10 \\ -\ 8 \\ \hline \end{array} \qquad \begin{array}{r} 10 \\ -\ 4 \\ \hline \end{array} \qquad \begin{array}{r} 10 \\ -\ 1 \\ \hline \end{array} \qquad \begin{array}{r} 10 \\ -\ 7 \\ \hline \end{array} \qquad \begin{array}{r} 10 \\ -\ 3 \\ \hline \end{array}$$

$$\begin{array}{r} 10 \\ -\ 5 \\ \hline \end{array} \qquad \begin{array}{r} 10 \\ -\ 2 \\ \hline \end{array} \qquad \begin{array}{r} 10 \\ -\ 9 \\ \hline \end{array} \qquad \begin{array}{r} 10 \\ -\ 6 \\ \hline \end{array} \qquad \begin{array}{r} 10 \\ -\ 0 \\ \hline \end{array}$$

$$\begin{array}{r} 10 \\ -\ 10 \\ \hline \end{array} \qquad \begin{array}{r} 10 \\ -\ 5 \\ \hline \end{array} \qquad \begin{array}{r} 10 \\ -\ 9 \\ \hline \end{array} \qquad \begin{array}{r} 10 \\ -\ 6 \\ \hline \end{array} \qquad \begin{array}{r} 10 \\ -\ 2 \\ \hline \end{array}$$

$$\begin{array}{r} 10 \\ -\ 3 \\ \hline \end{array} \qquad \begin{array}{r} 10 \\ -\ 7 \\ \hline \end{array} \qquad \begin{array}{r} 10 \\ -\ 1 \\ \hline \end{array} \qquad \begin{array}{r} 10 \\ -\ 4 \\ \hline \end{array} \qquad \begin{array}{r} 10 \\ -\ 8 \\ \hline \end{array}$$

$$\begin{array}{r} 10 \\ -\ 10 \\ \hline \end{array} \qquad \begin{array}{r} 10 \\ -\ 0 \\ \hline \end{array} \qquad \begin{array}{r} 10 \\ -\ 6 \\ \hline \end{array} \qquad \begin{array}{r} 10 \\ -\ 4 \\ \hline \end{array} \qquad \begin{array}{r} 10 \\ -\ 8 \\ \hline \end{array}$$

Score: _____

ame •
  (Draw a 4-inch line segment.)

ate _____

ıy of the Week _____

1. Write the number ninety-seven four more times. How many digits did you use? _____

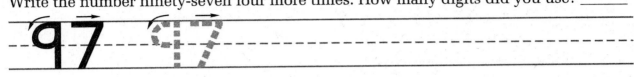

2. Daniel wrote five addition examples. Then he wrote three more addition examples. Show the examples he wrote.

_____
|                                                 |
|                                                 |
|                                                 |
|_____|

Write a number sentence to show how many examples Daniel wrote.

_____

How many examples is that? _____ examples

3. Point to the cake that is divided into halves.
Color one half of the cake red.
Point to the cake that is divided into thirds.
Color one third of the cake blue.
Point to the cake that is divided into sixths.
Color one sixth of the cake green.

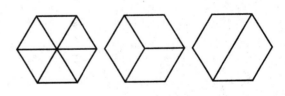

4. Color the pennies brown. How much money is this? _____

5. Show half past eleven on the clock.

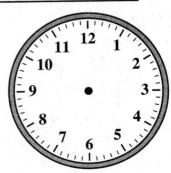

6. Find the answers.

10 − 6 = ____    10 − 8 = ____

10 − 1 = ____    10 − 3 = ____

1. Fill in the missing numbers.

| 81 | | | | | | | | | 90 |
|----|---|---|---|---|---|---|---|---|-----|
| 91 | | | | | | | | | 100 |

2. Cathy wrote four subtraction examples. Then she wrote two more subtraction examples. Show the examples she wrote.

   Write a number sentence to show how many examples Cathy wrote.

   _____

   How many examples is that? _____ examples

3. Point to the cake that is divided into sixths.
   Color one sixth of the cake green.
   Point to the cake that is divided into thirds.
   Color one third of the cake blue.
   Point to the cake that is divided into halves.
   Color one half of the cake red.

4. Color the pennies brown. How much money is this? _____

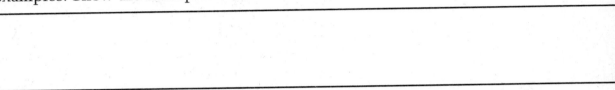

5. Show half past one on the clock.

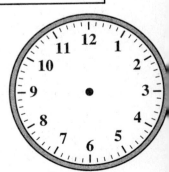

6. Find the answers.

   10 − 4 = ____    10 − 2 = ____

   10 − 9 = ____    10 − 7 = ____

```
    6          6          6
 + 10       + 10       + 9
```

```
    3          3          3
 + 10       + 10       + 9
```

```
    5          5          5
 + 10       + 10       + 9
```

```
    7          7          7
 + 10       + 10       + 9
```

```
    4          4          4
 + 10       + 10       + 9
```

```
   10         10          9
 +  3       +  3       + 3
```

```
   10         10          9
 +  5       +  5       + 5
```

```
   10         10          9
 +  7       +  7       + 7
```

```
   10         10          9
 +  4       +  4       + 4
```

```
   10         10          9
 +  6       +  6       + 6
```

$$
\begin{array}{r} 4 \\ + 9 \\ \hline \end{array}
\qquad
\begin{array}{r} 6 \\ + 9 \\ \hline \end{array}
\qquad
\begin{array}{r} 8 \\ + 9 \\ \hline \end{array}
\qquad
\begin{array}{r} 1 \\ + 9 \\ \hline \end{array}
\qquad
\begin{array}{r} 3 \\ + 9 \\ \hline \end{array}
$$

$$
\begin{array}{r} 2 \\ + 9 \\ \hline \end{array}
\qquad
\begin{array}{r} 7 \\ + 9 \\ \hline \end{array}
\qquad
\begin{array}{r} 9 \\ + 9 \\ \hline \end{array}
\qquad
\begin{array}{r} 5 \\ + 9 \\ \hline \end{array}
\qquad
\begin{array}{r} 0 \\ + 9 \\ \hline \end{array}
$$

$$
\begin{array}{r} 6 \\ + 9 \\ \hline \end{array}
\qquad
\begin{array}{r} 9 \\ + 9 \\ \hline \end{array}
\qquad
\begin{array}{r} 2 \\ + 9 \\ \hline \end{array}
\qquad
\begin{array}{r} 7 \\ + 9 \\ \hline \end{array}
\qquad
\begin{array}{r} 4 \\ + 9 \\ \hline \end{array}
$$

$$
\begin{array}{r} 9 \\ + 5 \\ \hline \end{array}
\qquad
\begin{array}{r} 9 \\ + 1 \\ \hline \end{array}
\qquad
\begin{array}{r} 9 \\ + 8 \\ \hline \end{array}
\qquad
\begin{array}{r} 9 \\ + 3 \\ \hline \end{array}
\qquad
\begin{array}{r} 9 \\ + 6 \\ \hline \end{array}
$$

$$
\begin{array}{r} 9 \\ + 8 \\ \hline \end{array}
\qquad
\begin{array}{r} 9 \\ + 0 \\ \hline \end{array}
\qquad
\begin{array}{r} 9 \\ + 5 \\ \hline \end{array}
\qquad
\begin{array}{r} 9 \\ + 7 \\ \hline \end{array}
\qquad
\begin{array}{r} 9 \\ + 3 \\ \hline \end{array}
$$

Score: _____

Name ● _____

(Draw a 3-inch line segment.)

Date _____

Day of the Week _____

1. Write the number ninety-eight four more times. How many digits did you use? _____

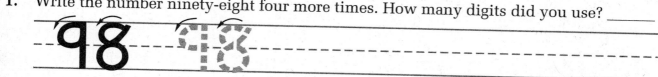

2. Billy's dad made a dozen muffins for breakfast. Billy's family ate ten muffins. Draw a picture and write a number sentence to show what happened.

Number sentence _____

How many muffins are left? _____ muffins

3. Point to the circle that is divided into thirds.
Color one third blue.

Point to the circle that is divided into halves.
Color one half red.

Point to the circle that is divided into sixths.
Color one sixth green.

Point to the circle that is divided into fourths.
Color one fourth orange.

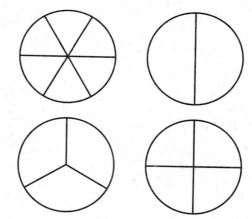

4. Find the answers.

$$\begin{array}{cc} 6 \\ + 10 \\ \hline \end{array} \qquad \begin{array}{cc} 6 \\ + 9 \\ \hline \end{array} \qquad \begin{array}{cc} 4 \\ + 10 \\ \hline \end{array} \qquad \begin{array}{cc} 4 \\ + 9 \\ \hline \end{array} \qquad \begin{array}{cc} 7 \\ + 10 \\ \hline \end{array} \qquad \begin{array}{cc} 7 \\ + 9 \\ \hline \end{array}$$

5. Work with a partner to measure the distance from the floor to the doorknob of your classroom door.

About how many feet from the floor is the doorknob? _____ feet

08Wa

Name _____

Date _____

1. Write the numbers that are one more than each number.

    9, _____          17, _____          26, _____

2. Jessie's mom poured a dozen glasses of orange juice. The children drank nine glasses of juice. Draw a picture and write a number sentence to show what happened.

    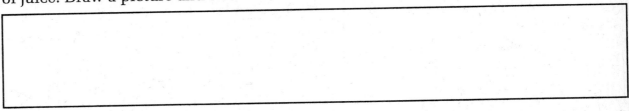

    Number sentence _____

    How many glasses of juice are left? _____ glasses of juice

3. Point to the square that is divided into thirds. Color one third blue.

    Point to the square that is divided into halves. Color one half red.

    Point to the square that is divided into sixths. Color one sixth green.

    Point to the square that is divided into fourths. Color one fourth orange.

    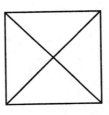
    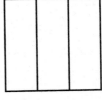

    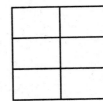

4. Find the answers.

    $$\begin{array}{r} 5 \\ + 10 \\ \hline \end{array} \qquad \begin{array}{r} 5 \\ + 9 \\ \hline \end{array} \qquad \begin{array}{r} 3 \\ + 10 \\ \hline \end{array} \qquad \begin{array}{r} 3 \\ + 9 \\ \hline \end{array} \qquad \begin{array}{r} 8 \\ + 10 \\ \hline \end{array} \qquad \begin{array}{r} 8 \\ + 9 \\ \hline \end{array}$$

5. Measure the length of your bed from the head of the bed to the foot of the bed.

    About how many feet long is your bed? _____ feet

| Container | Estimate | Actual |
|-----------|----------|--------|
| | _____ cups | _____ cups |
| | _____ cups | _____ cups |
| | _____ cups | _____ cups |

Name _____

$$\begin{array}{r} 4 \\ +\ 9 \\ \hline \end{array} \qquad \begin{array}{r} 6 \\ +\ 9 \\ \hline \end{array} \qquad \begin{array}{r} 8 \\ +\ 9 \\ \hline \end{array} \qquad \begin{array}{r} 1 \\ +\ 9 \\ \hline \end{array} \qquad \begin{array}{r} 3 \\ +\ 9 \\ \hline \end{array}$$

$$\begin{array}{r} 2 \\ +\ 9 \\ \hline \end{array} \qquad \begin{array}{r} 7 \\ +\ 9 \\ \hline \end{array} \qquad \begin{array}{r} 9 \\ +\ 9 \\ \hline \end{array} \qquad \begin{array}{r} 5 \\ +\ 9 \\ \hline \end{array} \qquad \begin{array}{r} 0 \\ +\ 9 \\ \hline \end{array}$$

$$\begin{array}{r} 6 \\ +\ 9 \\ \hline \end{array} \qquad \begin{array}{r} 9 \\ +\ 9 \\ \hline \end{array} \qquad \begin{array}{r} 2 \\ +\ 9 \\ \hline \end{array} \qquad \begin{array}{r} 7 \\ +\ 9 \\ \hline \end{array} \qquad \begin{array}{r} 4 \\ +\ 9 \\ \hline \end{array}$$

$$\begin{array}{r} 9 \\ +\ 5 \\ \hline \end{array} \qquad \begin{array}{r} 9 \\ +\ 1 \\ \hline \end{array} \qquad \begin{array}{r} 9 \\ +\ 8 \\ \hline \end{array} \qquad \begin{array}{r} 9 \\ +\ 3 \\ \hline \end{array} \qquad \begin{array}{r} 9 \\ +\ 6 \\ \hline \end{array}$$

$$\begin{array}{r} 9 \\ +\ 8 \\ \hline \end{array} \qquad \begin{array}{r} 9 \\ +\ 0 \\ \hline \end{array} \qquad \begin{array}{r} 9 \\ +\ 5 \\ \hline \end{array} \qquad \begin{array}{r} 9 \\ +\ 7 \\ \hline \end{array} \qquad \begin{array}{r} 9 \\ +\ 3 \\ \hline \end{array}$$

Score: _____

Name _____
    (Draw a 3-inch line segment.)

Date _____

Day of the Week _____

1. Write the number ninety-nine three more times. How many digits did you use? _____

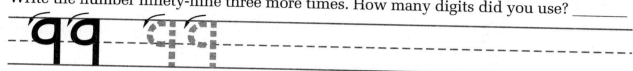

2. Ronisha had eight pieces of banana on her cereal. She ate four pieces. Draw a picture and write a number sentence to show what happened.

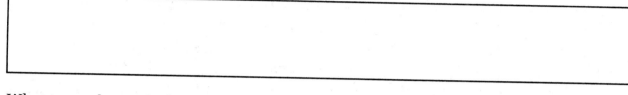

    What type of story is this?    some, some more    some, some went away

    Number sentence _____

    How many pieces of banana does she have left to eat? _____ pieces

3. Sharon had 34 pennies. She put them in groups of 10 on this mat. Draw the pennies to show what she did.

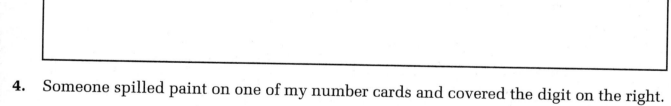

4. Someone spilled paint on one of my number cards and covered the digit on the right.

    Which number card has paint on it? _____

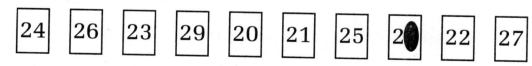

| 24 | 26 | 23 | 29 | 20 | 21 | 25 | 2● | 22 | 27 |

5. Choose four even numbers. Add 9 to each number.

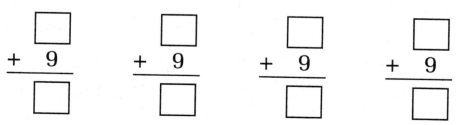

1. Write the number that is one less than each number.

   _____ , 7          _____ , 15          _____ , 23

2. Gina put 6 strawberries on her cereal. She ate 3 strawberries. Draw a picture and write a number sentence to show what happened.

   _____

   What type of story is this?     some, some more     some, some went away

   Number sentence _____

   How many strawberries does she have left to eat? _____ strawberries

3. Harry had 43 pennies. He put them in groups of 10 on this mat. Draw the pennies to show what he did.

   _____

4. Someone spilled paint on one of my number cards and covered the digit on the right.

   Which number card has paint on it? _____

   | 39 | 32 | 35 | 31 | 3● | 33 | 36 | 30 | 38 | 34 |

5. Choose four odd numbers. Add 9 to each number.

   ☐          ☐          ☐          ☐
   + 9        + 9        + 9        + 9
   ─────      ─────      ─────      ─────
   ☐          ☐          ☐          ☐

   Parent: Ask your child to find a gallon, liter, and quart container at home. If possible, allow them to count the number of cups of water needed to fill each container.

Name _____

Date _____

1. Ms. Allen bought a dozen eggs. She used three eggs to make a cake for her class. Draw a picture and write a number sentence to show how many eggs she has left.

Number sentence _____

How many eggs does she have left? _____ eggs

2. Draw a 4-inch line segment.

•

3. How much money is this? _____

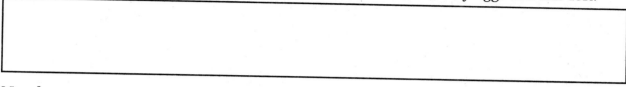

4. Fill in the missing numbers.

5. Draw congruent shapes on the geoboards.

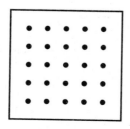 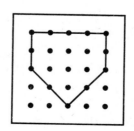 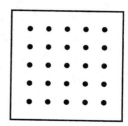

1-110Aa

$$
\begin{array}{r} 1 \\ + 9 \\ \hline \end{array}
\qquad
\begin{array}{r} 9 \\ + 8 \\ \hline \end{array}
\qquad
\begin{array}{r} 9 \\ + 7 \\ \hline \end{array}
\qquad
\begin{array}{r} 9 \\ + 9 \\ \hline \end{array}
\qquad
\begin{array}{r} 9 \\ + 2 \\ \hline \end{array}
$$

$$
\begin{array}{r} 9 \\ + 3 \\ \hline \end{array}
\qquad
\begin{array}{r} 4 \\ + 9 \\ \hline \end{array}
\qquad
\begin{array}{r} 9 \\ + 8 \\ \hline \end{array}
\qquad
\begin{array}{r} 2 \\ + 9 \\ \hline \end{array}
\qquad
\begin{array}{r} 3 \\ + 9 \\ \hline \end{array}
$$

$$
\begin{array}{r} 9 \\ + 2 \\ \hline \end{array}
\qquad
\begin{array}{r} 6 \\ + 9 \\ \hline \end{array}
\qquad
\begin{array}{r} 7 \\ + 9 \\ \hline \end{array}
\qquad
\begin{array}{r} 9 \\ + 0 \\ \hline \end{array}
\qquad
\begin{array}{r} 8 \\ + 9 \\ \hline \end{array}
$$

$$
\begin{array}{r} 3 \\ + 9 \\ \hline \end{array}
\qquad
\begin{array}{r} 9 \\ + 4 \\ \hline \end{array}
\qquad
\begin{array}{r} 9 \\ + 6 \\ \hline \end{array}
\qquad
\begin{array}{r} 2 \\ + 9 \\ \hline \end{array}
\qquad
\begin{array}{r} 9 \\ + 9 \\ \hline \end{array}
$$

$$
\begin{array}{r} 9 \\ + 5 \\ \hline \end{array}
\qquad
\begin{array}{r} 0 \\ + 9 \\ \hline \end{array}
\qquad
\begin{array}{r} 5 \\ + 9 \\ \hline \end{array}
\qquad
\begin{array}{r} 9 \\ + 1 \\ \hline \end{array}
\qquad
\begin{array}{r} 9 \\ + 4 \\ \hline \end{array}
$$

Score: _____

Name _____  •
(Draw a 3-inch line segment.)

Date _____

Day of the Week _____

1.  Write the number one hundred 3 more times.

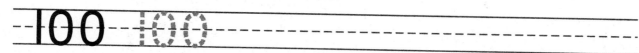

2.  Jeanne counted 26 pennies. She put them in groups of 10. Draw the pennies.

    Sherrie gave her 10 more pennies. Draw the pennies Sherrie gave Jeanne.
    Write a number sentence to show how many pennies Jeanne has now.

    Number sentence _____  Answer _____ pennies

3.  Cross out the cards you cannot put where the **A** is.

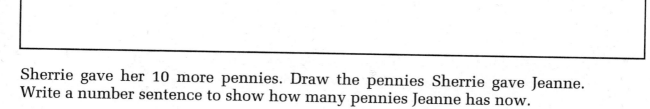

4.  How much money is this? _____

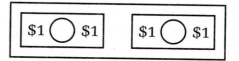

5.  Find the total on each receipt.

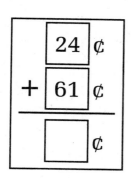
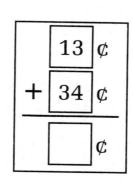
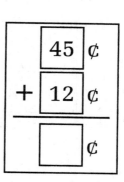

Name _____

Date _____

**1.** Write a number that is between 46 and 52.

46 ☐ 52

**2.** Laura counted 32 pennies. She put them in groups of 10. Draw the pennies.

☐

Maureen gave her 10 more pennies. Draw the pennies Maureen gave Laura.
Write a number sentence to show how many pennies Laura has now.

Number sentence _____   Answer _____ pennies

**3.** Cross out the cards you cannot put where the **B** is.

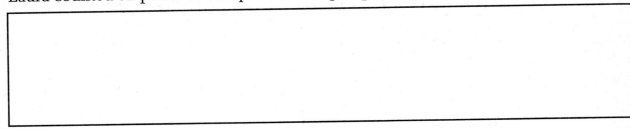

| 52 | 58 | B | 64 | 71 |   | 63 | 54 | 69 | 61 | 48 | 59 | 66 |

**4.** How much money is this?

_____

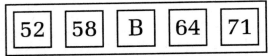

$1 ◯ $1    $1 ◯ $1

$1 ◯ $1

**5.** Find the total on each receipt.

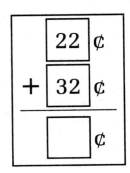

```
   22 ¢
 + 32 ¢
 _____
  ☐  ¢
```

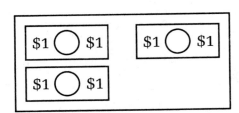

```
   65 ¢
 + 21 ¢
 _____
  ☐  ¢
```

```
   74 ¢
 + 25 ¢
 _____
  ☐  ¢
```

Name _____

$$\begin{array}{r} 1 \\ +\ 9 \\ \hline \end{array} \qquad \begin{array}{r} 9 \\ +\ 8 \\ \hline \end{array} \qquad \begin{array}{r} 9 \\ +\ 7 \\ \hline \end{array} \qquad \begin{array}{r} 9 \\ +\ 9 \\ \hline \end{array} \qquad \begin{array}{r} 9 \\ +\ 2 \\ \hline \end{array}$$

$$\begin{array}{r} 9 \\ +\ 3 \\ \hline \end{array} \qquad \begin{array}{r} 4 \\ +\ 9 \\ \hline \end{array} \qquad \begin{array}{r} 9 \\ +\ 8 \\ \hline \end{array} \qquad \begin{array}{r} 2 \\ +\ 9 \\ \hline \end{array} \qquad \begin{array}{r} 3 \\ +\ 9 \\ \hline \end{array}$$

$$\begin{array}{r} 9 \\ +\ 2 \\ \hline \end{array} \qquad \begin{array}{r} 6 \\ +\ 9 \\ \hline \end{array} \qquad \begin{array}{r} 7 \\ +\ 9 \\ \hline \end{array} \qquad \begin{array}{r} 9 \\ +\ 0 \\ \hline \end{array} \qquad \begin{array}{r} 8 \\ +\ 9 \\ \hline \end{array}$$

$$\begin{array}{r} 3 \\ +\ 9 \\ \hline \end{array} \qquad \begin{array}{r} 9 \\ +\ 4 \\ \hline \end{array} \qquad \begin{array}{r} 9 \\ +\ 6 \\ \hline \end{array} \qquad \begin{array}{r} 2 \\ +\ 9 \\ \hline \end{array} \qquad \begin{array}{r} 9 \\ +\ 9 \\ \hline \end{array}$$

$$\begin{array}{r} 9 \\ +\ 5 \\ \hline \end{array} \qquad \begin{array}{r} 0 \\ +\ 9 \\ \hline \end{array} \qquad \begin{array}{r} 5 \\ +\ 9 \\ \hline \end{array} \qquad \begin{array}{r} 9 \\ +\ 1 \\ \hline \end{array} \qquad \begin{array}{r} 9 \\ +\ 4 \\ \hline \end{array}$$

Score: _____

Name _____ •
(Draw a 4-inch line segment.)

Date _____

Day of the Week _____

**LESSON 112A**

**Math 1**

1. Write the number one hundred one 4 more times.

   $\text{101}$ ────────────────────────────────

2. Evie read 21 pages of her book on Monday. On Tuesday, she read 10 more pages.

   What kind of story is this?          some, some more          some, some went away

   Write a number sentence to find how many pages she read altogether.

   Number sentence _____          Answer _____ pages

3. Each vegetable is cut into how many pieces?

   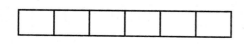      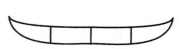

   _____ pieces          _____ pieces          _____ pieces

4. Circle a dozen donuts.
   Color a half dozen brown
   to show that they are chocolate.

   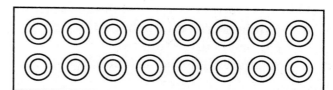

5. Use the classroom calendar to answer these questions.

   What was the date of the first Tuesday of this month? _____

   What was yesterday's date? _____

   What day of the week will it be tomorrow? _____

6. Find the answers.

   $59 + 10 = $ ____          $74 + 10 = $ ____          $16 + 10 = $ ____

7. Find the answers.

$$
\begin{array}{cccccc}
7 & 4 & 5 & 8 & 5 & 9 \\
+\,9 & +\,9 & +\,9 & -\,2 & -\,2 & -\,2 \\
\hline
\end{array}
$$

Date _____

1. Write the numbers that are one less and one more than each number.

   _____ , 19, _____          _____ , 40, _____

2. Curtis read 36 pages of his book on Saturday. On Sunday, he read 10 more pages.

   What kind of story is this?      some, some more          some, some went away

   Write a number sentence to find how many pages he read altogether.

   Number sentence _____      Answer _____ pages

3. Each shape is divided into how many pieces?

   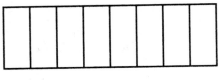   

   _____ pieces          _____ pieces          _____ pieces

4. Circle a dozen cupcakes.
   Color a half dozen brown
   to show that they are chocolate.

5. What will be the date tomorrow? _____

6. Find the answers.

   62 + 10 = ____      36 + 10 = ____      11 + 10 = ____

7. Find the answers.

   | 6 | 8 | 3 | 7 | 10 | 6 |
   |---|---|---|---|----|---|
   | + 9 | + 9 | + 9 | − 2 | − 2 | − 2 |

| | | | | |
|---|---|---|---|---|
| 5<br>+ 1 | 8<br>+ 9 | 9<br>+ 5 | 5<br>+ 5 | 4<br>+ 9 |
| 9<br>+ 9 | 2<br>+ 9 | 7<br>+ 2 | 3<br>+ 7 | 7<br>+ 7 |
| 5<br>+ 4 | 4<br>+ 6 | 3<br>+ 3 | 4<br>+ 3 | 8<br>+ 2 |
| 6<br>+ 6 | 7<br>+ 8 | 9<br>+ 0 | 5<br>+ 9 | 3<br>+ 9 |
| 3<br>+ 7 | 4<br>+ 9 | 0<br>+ 5 | 8<br>+ 8 | 9<br>+ 6 |

Score: _____

Name ●
    (Draw a 3-inch line segment.)

Date _____

Day of the Week _____

1. Write the number one hundred two 3 more times.

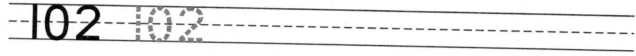

2. Ellen has 10 corn chips.
   She will share them equally with Anthony.
   Draw a plate for each child.
   Draw the corn chips on the plates to show how
   many corn chips each child will have.

   How many corn chips
   will Anthony have? _____ corn chips

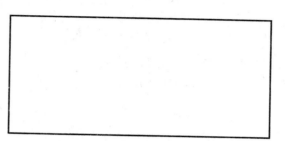

3. Color the pennies brown. Count the money. _____

4. Show half past seven on the clocks.

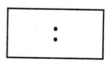

5. Write two observations about
   your classroom vegetable graph.

   1. _____

   2. _____

6. Find the answers.

   53 + 10 = ____      21 + 10 = ____      84 + 10 = ____

Name _____

Date _____

1. Finish the number pattern.

   6, 16, 26, 36, _____ , _____ , _____ , _____ , _____ , __

2. Charlie has 8 markers.
   He will share them equally with James.
   Draw the markers in the boxes to show
   how many markers each child will have.

   How many markers
   will James have? _____ markers

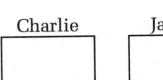

Charlie      James

3. Color the pennies brown. Count the money. _____

4. Show half past one on the clocks.

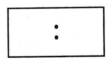

Vegetables We Like

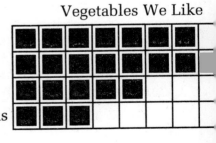

tomatoes

carrots

celery

mushrooms

5. The children in Mrs. Ireland's
   class made this graph.

   Write two things you know about
   the children in Mrs. Ireland's class.

   1. _____

   2. _____

6. Find the answers.

   $24 + 10 =$ _____      $35 + 10 =$ _____      $83 + 10 =$ _

$$\begin{array}{r} 5 \\ + 1 \\ \hline \end{array} \qquad \begin{array}{r} 8 \\ + 9 \\ \hline \end{array} \qquad \begin{array}{r} 9 \\ + 5 \\ \hline \end{array} \qquad \begin{array}{r} 5 \\ + 5 \\ \hline \end{array} \qquad \begin{array}{r} 4 \\ + 9 \\ \hline \end{array}$$

$$\begin{array}{r} 9 \\ + 9 \\ \hline \end{array} \qquad \begin{array}{r} 2 \\ + 9 \\ \hline \end{array} \qquad \begin{array}{r} 7 \\ + 2 \\ \hline \end{array} \qquad \begin{array}{r} 3 \\ + 7 \\ \hline \end{array} \qquad \begin{array}{r} 7 \\ + 7 \\ \hline \end{array}$$

$$\begin{array}{r} 5 \\ + 4 \\ \hline \end{array} \qquad \begin{array}{r} 4 \\ + 6 \\ \hline \end{array} \qquad \begin{array}{r} 3 \\ + 3 \\ \hline \end{array} \qquad \begin{array}{r} 4 \\ + 3 \\ \hline \end{array} \qquad \begin{array}{r} 8 \\ + 2 \\ \hline \end{array}$$

$$\begin{array}{r} 6 \\ + 6 \\ \hline \end{array} \qquad \begin{array}{r} 7 \\ + 8 \\ \hline \end{array} \qquad \begin{array}{r} 9 \\ + 0 \\ \hline \end{array} \qquad \begin{array}{r} 5 \\ + 9 \\ \hline \end{array} \qquad \begin{array}{r} 3 \\ + 9 \\ \hline \end{array}$$

$$\begin{array}{r} 3 \\ + 7 \\ \hline \end{array} \qquad \begin{array}{r} 4 \\ + 9 \\ \hline \end{array} \qquad \begin{array}{r} 0 \\ + 5 \\ \hline \end{array} \qquad \begin{array}{r} 8 \\ + 8 \\ \hline \end{array} \qquad \begin{array}{r} 9 \\ + 6 \\ \hline \end{array}$$

Score: _____

Name .
(Draw a 3-inch line segment.)

Date _____

Day of the Week _____

1. Write the number one hundred three 2 more times.

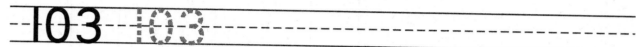

2. The children in Room 2 had five frogs.
   They gave one frog to the children in Room 3.
   Draw a picture and write a number sentence to show what happened.

   ```
   ┌────────────────────────────────────────┐
   │                                        │
   │                                        │
   │                                        │
   │                                        │
   └────────────────────────────────────────┘
   ```

   Number sentence _____

   How many frogs do the children in Room 2 have now? _____ frogs

3. Color the pennies brown. Count the money. _____

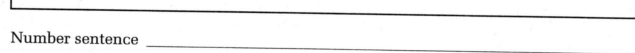

4. Finish the number pattern.

   4, 14, 24, _____ , _____ , _____ , _____ , _____ , _____ , _____

5. Find the answers.

$$\begin{array}{cccccc} 6 & 9 & 10 & 10 & 9 & 6 \\ +\ 9 & +\ 4 & -\ 6 & -\ 3 & -\ 2 & -\ 2 \end{array}$$

1. Fill in the missing numbers.

| | | | 74 | | | | | 80 |
|---|---|---|---|---|---|---|---|---|
| | | | | 86 | | | | |

2. The children in Room 4 had seven fish.
   They gave two fish to the children in Room 1.
   Draw a picture and write a number sentence to show what happened.

   Number sentence _____

   How many fish do the children in Room 4 have now? _____ fish

3. Color the pennies brown. Count the money. _____

4. Finish the number pattern.

   8, 18, 28, _____ , _____ , _____ , _____ , _____ , _____ , _____

5. Find the answers.

```
    5          9         10         10          5          7
  + 9        + 7        - 4        - 7        - 2        - 2
  ___        ___        ___        ___        ___        ___
```

Name ● 

(Draw a 4-inch line segment.)

Date _____

Day of the Week _____

1. Maurice had 9 rocks in his collection. He found 2 more rocks for his collection. Draw a picture and write a number sentence to show the rocks in his collection.

Number sentence _____

How many rocks are in his collection now? _____ rocks

2. Danny has 6 dimes.
He will share them equally with Tricia.
Draw the dimes in the boxes to show
how many dimes each child will have.

Danny      Tricia

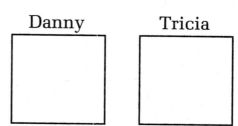

How many dimes
will Tricia have? _____ dimes

3. Color the pennies brown. Count the money. _____

4. Finish the patterns.

6, 8, 10, _____ , _____ , _____ , _____ , _____

24, 23, 22, _____ , _____ , _____ , _____ , _____

5. Find the answers.

$$\begin{array}{ccccccc} 6 & 9 & 7 & 6 & 10 & 7 & 6 \\ +2 & -1 & +7 & +9 & -4 & -2 & +5 \end{array}$$

-115Aa

| | | | | |
|---|---|---|---|---|
| 5<br>+ 1 | 8<br>+ 9 | 9<br>+ 5 | 5<br>+ 5 | 4<br>+ 9 |
| 9<br>+ 9 | 2<br>+ 9 | 7<br>+ 2 | 3<br>+ 7 | 7<br>+ 7 |
| 5<br>+ 4 | 4<br>+ 6 | 3<br>+ 3 | 4<br>+ 3 | 8<br>+ 2 |
| 6<br>+ 6 | 7<br>+ 8 | 9<br>+ 0 | 5<br>+ 9 | 3<br>+ 9 |
| 3<br>+ 7 | 4<br>+ 9 | 0<br>+ 5 | 8<br>+ 8 | 9<br>+ 6 |

Score: _____

Name ● 

(Draw a 2-inch line segment.)

Date _____

Day of the Week _____

1. Write the number one hundred four 2 more times.

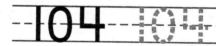

2. Michelle wrote a two-digit number on a piece of paper.
She gave the children the following clues to help them guess her secret number.
Michelle said, "The digits I used are 5 and 3."

Write the two possible numbers. _____ _____

Michelle said, "The number is between 29 and 41." Circle Michelle's secret number.

3. Circle the coins Frank can use to pay for the pencil.

17¢

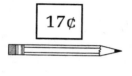        

4. Krista put the linking cubes in trains of 10.
How many linking cubes does she have?

_____ linking cubes

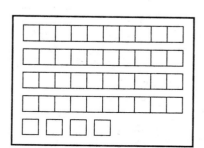

5. Draw tally marks to show the number of chairs in your classroom.

How many chairs are there? _____

6. Find the answers.

79 + 10 = ____    8 + 10 = ____    22 + 10 = ____

Name _____

Date _____

1. Fill in the missing numbers.

45, 44, 43, _____ , _____ , _____ , _____ , _____

5, 10, 15, _____ , _____ , _____ , _____ , _____

2. Sam wrote a two-digit number on a piece of paper.
   He gave the children the following clues to help them guess his secret number.
   Sam said, "The digits I used are 7 and 2."

   Write the two possible numbers. _____   _____

   Sam said, "The number is between 18 and 28." Circle Sam's secret number.

3. Circle the coins Paula can use to pay for the ruler.

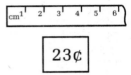        

4. Martha put the linking cubes in trains of 10.
   How many linking cubes does she have?

   _____ linking cubes

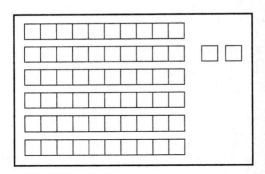

5. Draw tally marks to show the number of chairs in your home.

   How many chairs are there? _____

6. Find the answers.

   88 + 10 = ____      6 + 10 = ____      45 + 10 = ____

| | | | | |
|---|---|---|---|---|
| 7<br>+ 5 | 5<br>+ 3 | 4<br>+ 7 | 8<br>+ 5 | 3<br>+ 6 |
| 6<br>+ 8 | 7<br>+ 4 | 8<br>+ 3 | 3<br>+ 5 | 7<br>+ 5 |
| 6<br>+ 3 | 5<br>+ 7 | 8<br>+ 6 | 4<br>+ 7 | 8<br>+ 5 |
| 3<br>+ 8 | 5<br>+ 3 | 6<br>+ 8 | 7<br>+ 4 | 3<br>+ 6 |
| 8<br>+ 5 | 6<br>+ 3 | 3<br>+ 5 | 8<br>+ 6 | 3<br>+ 8 |

Score: _____

Name _____

5 + 3 = _____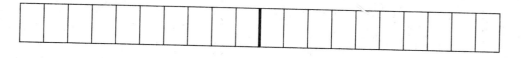

6 + 3 = _____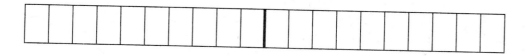

8 + 3 = _____

7 + 4 = _____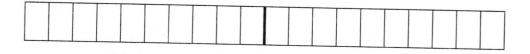

7 + 5 = _____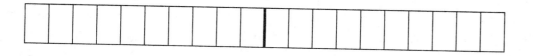

8 + 4 = _____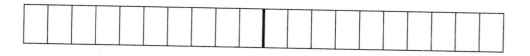

8 + 5 = _____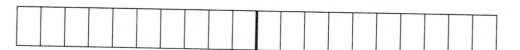

8 + 6 = _____

116Ma

Name _____ •
    (Draw a 4-inch line segment.)

Date _____

Day of the Week _____

**LESSON 116A**

**Math 1**

1. Write the number one hundred five 3 more times.

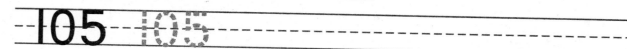

2. Nishaun counted 35 linking cubes. He put them in trains of 10. Draw the linking cubes.

Taylor gave him 10 more linking cubes. Draw the linking cubes Taylor gave Nishaun. Write a number sentence to show how many linking cubes Nishaun has now.

Number sentence _____    Answer _____ linking cubes

3. Color the pennies brown. Count the money. _____

4. Finish the pattern.

    9, 19, 29, _____ , _____ , _____ , _____ , _____ , _____ , _____

5. Show half past three on the clock.

6. Fill in the answers on the receipts.

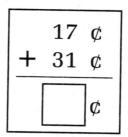

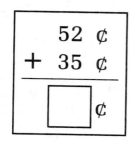

Name _____

Date _____

1. Circle the congruent shapes. (Congruent shapes are the same size and shape.)

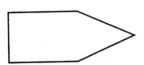  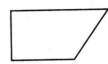 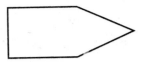 

2. Katie counted 27 linking cubes. She put them into trains of 10. Draw the linking cubes.

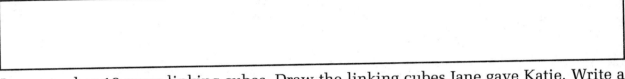

Jane gave her 10 more linking cubes. Draw the linking cubes Jane gave Katie. Write a number sentence to show how many linking cubes Katie has now.

Number sentence _____     Answer _____ linking cubes

3. Color the pennies brown. Count the money. _____

4. Finish the pattern.

   8, 18, 28, ____ , ____ , ____ , ____ , ____ , ____ , ____

5. Show half past seven on the clock.

6. Fill in the answers on the receipts.

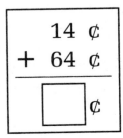

| 14 ¢ |
| + 64 ¢ |
| ☐ ¢ |

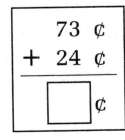

| 73 ¢ |
| + 24 ¢ |
| ☐ ¢ |

Name _____

1.

_____ centimeters

2.

_____ centimeters

3.

_____ centimeters

4.

_____ centimeters

5.

_____ centimeters

6.

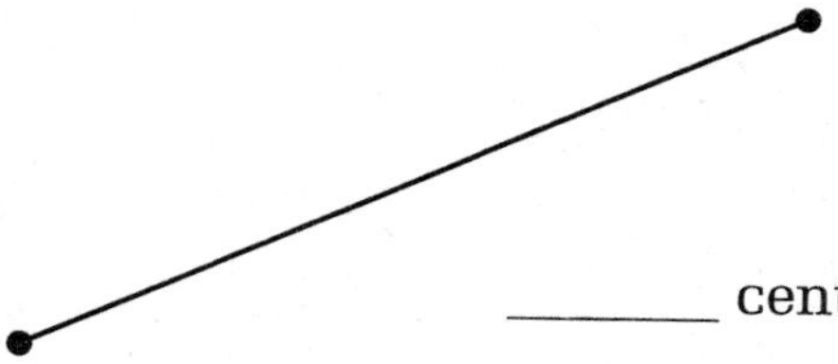

_____ centimeters

$$
\begin{array}{r} 7 \\ + 5 \\ \hline \end{array}
\qquad
\begin{array}{r} 5 \\ + 3 \\ \hline \end{array}
\qquad
\begin{array}{r} 4 \\ + 7 \\ \hline \end{array}
\qquad
\begin{array}{r} 8 \\ + 5 \\ \hline \end{array}
\qquad
\begin{array}{r} 3 \\ + 6 \\ \hline \end{array}
$$

$$
\begin{array}{r} 6 \\ + 8 \\ \hline \end{array}
\qquad
\begin{array}{r} 7 \\ + 4 \\ \hline \end{array}
\qquad
\begin{array}{r} 8 \\ + 3 \\ \hline \end{array}
\qquad
\begin{array}{r} 3 \\ + 5 \\ \hline \end{array}
\qquad
\begin{array}{r} 7 \\ + 5 \\ \hline \end{array}
$$

$$
\begin{array}{r} 6 \\ + 3 \\ \hline \end{array}
\qquad
\begin{array}{r} 5 \\ + 7 \\ \hline \end{array}
\qquad
\begin{array}{r} 8 \\ + 6 \\ \hline \end{array}
\qquad
\begin{array}{r} 4 \\ + 7 \\ \hline \end{array}
\qquad
\begin{array}{r} 8 \\ + 5 \\ \hline \end{array}
$$

$$
\begin{array}{r} 3 \\ + 8 \\ \hline \end{array}
\qquad
\begin{array}{r} 5 \\ + 3 \\ \hline \end{array}
\qquad
\begin{array}{r} 6 \\ + 8 \\ \hline \end{array}
\qquad
\begin{array}{r} 7 \\ + 4 \\ \hline \end{array}
\qquad
\begin{array}{r} 3 \\ + 6 \\ \hline \end{array}
$$

$$
\begin{array}{r} 8 \\ + 5 \\ \hline \end{array}
\qquad
\begin{array}{r} 6 \\ + 3 \\ \hline \end{array}
\qquad
\begin{array}{r} 3 \\ + 5 \\ \hline \end{array}
\qquad
\begin{array}{r} 8 \\ + 6 \\ \hline \end{array}
\qquad
\begin{array}{r} 3 \\ + 8 \\ \hline \end{array}
$$

Score: _____

Name ●
(Draw an 11-centimeter line segment.)

Date _____

Day of the Week _____

1. Write the number one hundred six 4 more times.

  106   106   - - - - - - - - - - - - - - - - - -

2. Fill in the next three shapes
   and numbers on the calendar.

   What is the date of the
   first Monday in May? _____

   What is the date of the
   second Friday in May? _____

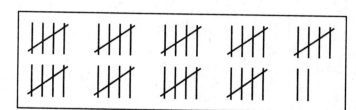

| May | | | | | | |
|---|---|---|---|---|---|---|
| Sunday | Monday | Tuesday | Wednesday | Thursday | Friday | Saturday |
|  |  |  | 1 | 2 | ③ | ④ |
| △5 | 6 | 7 | ⑧ | ⑨ | △10 | 11 |
| 12 | ⑬ |  |  |  |  |  |

3. Count the tally marks. _____

   卌 卌 卌 卌 卌
   卌 卌 卌 卌 ||

4. Color the cones blue.

   Color the spheres red.

5. Color the graph to show how many
   cones and spheres you colored.

   How many more cones
   than spheres did you color? _____

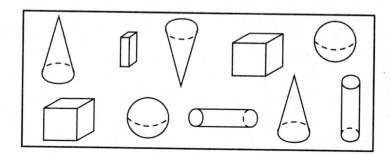

| cones |  |  |  |  |  |  |
|---|---|---|---|---|---|---|
| spheres |  |  |  |  |  |  |

6. Find the answers.

   10 − 6 = ____      10 − 2 = ____      7 + 9 = ____

   65 + 10 = ____     46 + 10 = ____     81 + 10 = ____

Name _____

Date _____

1.  Circle all the numbers that are between 42 and 55.

    41      59      47      21      53      43      56

2.  Fill in the next three shapes and numbers on the calendar.

    What is the date of the first Thursday in April? _____

    What is the date of the second Wednesday in April? _____

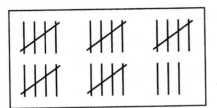

April

| Sunday | Monday | Tuesday | Wednesday | Thursday | Friday | Saturday |
|--------|--------|---------|-----------|----------|--------|----------|
|        |        | (1)     | 2         | 3        | (4)    | 5        |
| 6      | (7)    | 8       | 9         | (10)     | 11     | 12       |
| (13)   | 14     | 15      |           |          |        |          |

3.  Count the tally marks. _____

4.  Color the cones blue.

    Color the spheres red.

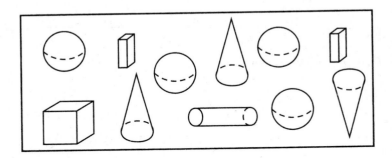

5.  Color the graph to show how many cones and spheres you colored.

    | cones   |  |  |  |  |  |  |
    |---------|--|--|--|--|--|--|
    | spheres |  |  |  |  |  |  |

    How many more spheres than cones did you color? _____

6.  Find the answers.

    10 − 4 = ____     10 − 7 = ____     4 + 9 = ____

    17 + 10 = ____     39 + 10 = ____     78 + 10 = ____

$$\begin{array}{r} 7 \\ + \ 5 \\ \hline \end{array} \qquad \begin{array}{r} 5 \\ + \ 3 \\ \hline \end{array} \qquad \begin{array}{r} 4 \\ + \ 7 \\ \hline \end{array} \qquad \begin{array}{r} 8 \\ + \ 5 \\ \hline \end{array} \qquad \begin{array}{r} 3 \\ + \ 6 \\ \hline \end{array}$$

$$\begin{array}{r} 6 \\ + \ 8 \\ \hline \end{array} \qquad \begin{array}{r} 7 \\ + \ 4 \\ \hline \end{array} \qquad \begin{array}{r} 8 \\ + \ 3 \\ \hline \end{array} \qquad \begin{array}{r} 3 \\ + \ 5 \\ \hline \end{array} \qquad \begin{array}{r} 7 \\ + \ 5 \\ \hline \end{array}$$

$$\begin{array}{r} 6 \\ + \ 3 \\ \hline \end{array} \qquad \begin{array}{r} 5 \\ + \ 7 \\ \hline \end{array} \qquad \begin{array}{r} 8 \\ + \ 6 \\ \hline \end{array} \qquad \begin{array}{r} 4 \\ + \ 7 \\ \hline \end{array} \qquad \begin{array}{r} 8 \\ + \ 5 \\ \hline \end{array}$$

$$\begin{array}{r} 3 \\ + \ 8 \\ \hline \end{array} \qquad \begin{array}{r} 5 \\ + \ 3 \\ \hline \end{array} \qquad \begin{array}{r} 6 \\ + \ 8 \\ \hline \end{array} \qquad \begin{array}{r} 7 \\ + \ 4 \\ \hline \end{array} \qquad \begin{array}{r} 3 \\ + \ 6 \\ \hline \end{array}$$

$$\begin{array}{r} 8 \\ + \ 5 \\ \hline \end{array} \qquad \begin{array}{r} 6 \\ + \ 3 \\ \hline \end{array} \qquad \begin{array}{r} 3 \\ + \ 5 \\ \hline \end{array} \qquad \begin{array}{r} 8 \\ + \ 6 \\ \hline \end{array} \qquad \begin{array}{r} 3 \\ + \ 8 \\ \hline \end{array}$$

Score: _____

Name ●
    (Draw a 9-centimeter line segment.)

Date _____

Day of the Week _____

1. Write the number one hundred seven 2 more times.

   107   107   ----------------------------------

2. Harvey cut out a half dozen paper hearts. Then he cut out two more paper hearts.
   Draw a picture and write a number sentence to show the hearts.

   ┌─────────────────────────────────────────────────┐
   │                                                 │
   │                                                 │
   │                                                 │
   │                                                 │
   │                                                 │
   └─────────────────────────────────────────────────┘

   Number sentence _____

   How many paper hearts did Harvey cut out altogether? _____ hearts

3. Circle the coins that Melinda can use to pay for the donut.

4. Circle the clock that shows half past one.

5. Measure this line segment using centimeters.

   ●————————————————————————————————————● _____ cm

6. Find the answers.

   5 + 7 = ____      4 + 7 = ____      6 + 8 = ____

   3 + 8 = ____      5 + 3 = ____      8 + 5 = ____

-118Wa

Name _____

Date _____

**1.** Put the number cards in order from least to greatest.

 42 51 39 47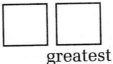

least          greatest

**2.** Carolyn had a half dozen pencils. She gave one pencil to Allison.
Draw a picture and write a number sentence to show what happened in this story.

Number sentence _____

How many pencils does Carolyn have now? _____ pencils

**3.** Circle the coins that Angelo can use to pay for the cupcake.

 32¢

**4.** Circle the clock that shows half past eleven.

**5.** Color one half red.
Color one third blue.
Color one sixth green.

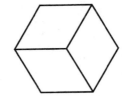 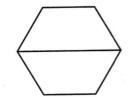 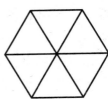

**6.** Find the answers.

3 + 5 = ____        7 + 4 = ____        4 + 8 = ____

6 + 8 = ____        8 + 3 = ____        5 + 7 = ____

$$
\begin{array}{r} 2 \\ + 8 \\ \hline \end{array}
\qquad
\begin{array}{r} 3 \\ + 5 \\ \hline \end{array}
\qquad
\begin{array}{r} 5 \\ + 6 \\ \hline \end{array}
\qquad
\begin{array}{r} 8 \\ + 3 \\ \hline \end{array}
\qquad
\begin{array}{r} 6 \\ + 8 \\ \hline \end{array}
$$

$$
\begin{array}{r} 3 \\ + 4 \\ \hline \end{array}
\qquad
\begin{array}{r} 7 \\ + 7 \\ \hline \end{array}
\qquad
\begin{array}{r} 1 \\ + 9 \\ \hline \end{array}
\qquad
\begin{array}{r} 6 \\ + 3 \\ \hline \end{array}
\qquad
\begin{array}{r} 4 \\ + 5 \\ \hline \end{array}
$$

$$
\begin{array}{r} 5 \\ + 7 \\ \hline \end{array}
\qquad
\begin{array}{r} 6 \\ + 9 \\ \hline \end{array}
\qquad
\begin{array}{r} 3 \\ + 4 \\ \hline \end{array}
\qquad
\begin{array}{r} 9 \\ + 9 \\ \hline \end{array}
\qquad
\begin{array}{r} 8 \\ + 5 \\ \hline \end{array}
$$

$$
\begin{array}{r} 6 \\ + 7 \\ \hline \end{array}
\qquad
\begin{array}{r} 7 \\ + 4 \\ \hline \end{array}
\qquad
\begin{array}{r} 8 \\ + 9 \\ \hline \end{array}
\qquad
\begin{array}{r} 3 \\ + 7 \\ \hline \end{array}
\qquad
\begin{array}{r} 5 \\ + 3 \\ \hline \end{array}
$$

$$
\begin{array}{r} 4 \\ + 4 \\ \hline \end{array}
\qquad
\begin{array}{r} 6 \\ + 5 \\ \hline \end{array}
\qquad
\begin{array}{r} 3 \\ + 6 \\ \hline \end{array}
\qquad
\begin{array}{r} 8 \\ + 3 \\ \hline \end{array}
\qquad
\begin{array}{r} 7 \\ + 6 \\ \hline \end{array}
$$

Score: _____

Name ●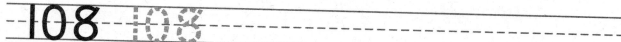

(Draw a 10-centimeter line segment.)

Date _____

Day of the Week _____

1. Write the number one hundred eight 3 more times.

   108  108  _ _ _ _ _ _ _ _ _ _ _ _ _ _ _ _ _ _ _ _ _ _ _ _

2. Amy had six dimes and two pennies. Her sister gave her three more dimes. Draw the coins.

   ```
   ┌────────────────────────────────────────────────┐
   │                                                │
   │                                                │
   │                                                │
   └────────────────────────────────────────────────┘
   ```

   How many dimes does Amy have now? _____ dimes

   How much money does she have altogether? _____

3. Circle all the shapes divided into fourths using an orange crayon.

   Color one fourth of each circled shape orange.

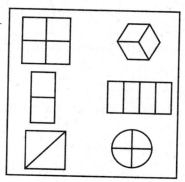

4. Color the cubes green.

   Color the cylinders orange.

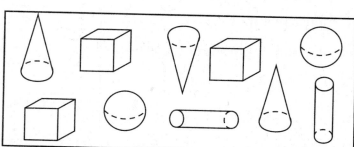

5. Color the graph to show how many cubes and cylinders you colored.

   How many more cubes than cylinders did you color? _____

   | cubes     |  |  |  |  |  |  |
   |-----------|--|--|--|--|--|--|
   | cylinders |  |  |  |  |  |  |

6. Find the answers.

   $63 - 10 =$ ____     $62 + 10 =$ ____     $48 - 10 =$ ____

   $14 + 10 =$ ____     $79 - 10 =$ ____     $36 + 10 =$ ____

-119Wa

1. Finish the patterns.

   100, 90, 80, 70, ___ , ___ , ___ , ___ , ___ , ___ , ___

   4, 6, 8, 10, ___ , ___ , ___ , ___ , ___ , ___ , ___

2. Alex had seven dimes and three pennies. He gave his brother two dimes. Draw the coins.

   How many dimes does Alex have now? _____ dimes

   How much money does he have altogether? _____

3. Circle all the shapes divided into halves using a green crayon.

   Color one half of each circled shape green.

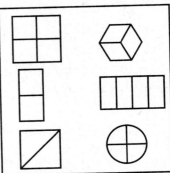

4. Color the cubes green.

   Color the cylinders orange.

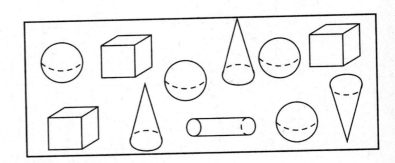

5. Color the graph to show how many cubes and cylinders you colored.

   How many more cubes than cylinders did you color? _____

   | cubes     |  |  |  |  |  |
   |-----------|--|--|--|--|--|
   | cylinders |  |  |  |  |  |

6. Find the answers.

   49 – 10 = ___     61 – 10 = ___     42 + 10 = ___

   21 + 10 = ___     18 + 10 = ___     93 – 10 = ___

Name _____

Date _____

**1.** Randy counted 24 pennies. He put them in groups of 10. Draw the pennies.

```




```

Philip gave him 10 more pennies. Draw the pennies Philip gave Randy.
Write a number sentence to show how many pennies Randy has now.

Number sentence _____  Answer _____ pennies

**2.** Cross out the cards you cannot put where the X is.

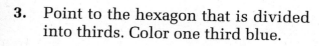     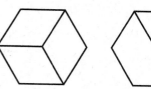

**3.** Point to the hexagon that is divided
into thirds. Color one third blue.

Point to the hexagon that is divided
in half. Color one half red.

Point to the hexagon that is divided
into sixths. Color one sixth green.

**4.** Find the answers.

35 + 10 = ____    14 + 10 = ____    83 + 10 = ____

**5.** Use the classroom calendar to answer these questions.

What was the date of the first Monday of this month? _____

What day of the week will it be tomorrow? _____

How many days are there in one week? _____

Name _____

**A.**

3 + 2 + 2 =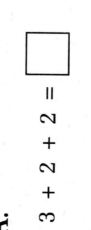

**B.**

1 + 8 + 2 = □

**C.**

2 + 5 + 3 = □

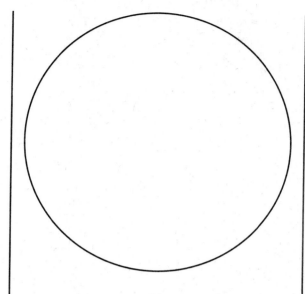

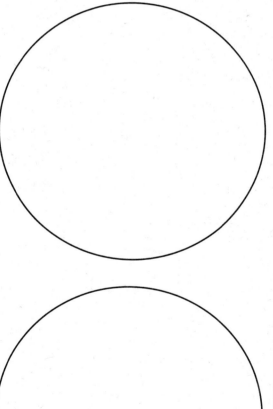

**D.**

```
   1
   8
+  9
─────
```
□

**E.**

```
   3
   6
+  4
─────
```
□

**F.**

```
   5
   2
+  4
─────
```
□

1-121a

$$\begin{array}{r} 2 \\ + 8 \\ \hline \end{array} \qquad \begin{array}{r} 3 \\ + 5 \\ \hline \end{array} \qquad \begin{array}{r} 5 \\ + 6 \\ \hline \end{array} \qquad \begin{array}{r} 8 \\ + 3 \\ \hline \end{array} \qquad \begin{array}{r} 6 \\ + 8 \\ \hline \end{array}$$

$$\begin{array}{r} 3 \\ + 4 \\ \hline \end{array} \qquad \begin{array}{r} 7 \\ + 7 \\ \hline \end{array} \qquad \begin{array}{r} 1 \\ + 9 \\ \hline \end{array} \qquad \begin{array}{r} 6 \\ + 3 \\ \hline \end{array} \qquad \begin{array}{r} 4 \\ + 5 \\ \hline \end{array}$$

$$\begin{array}{r} 5 \\ + 7 \\ \hline \end{array} \qquad \begin{array}{r} 6 \\ + 9 \\ \hline \end{array} \qquad \begin{array}{r} 3 \\ + 4 \\ \hline \end{array} \qquad \begin{array}{r} 9 \\ + 9 \\ \hline \end{array} \qquad \begin{array}{r} 8 \\ + 5 \\ \hline \end{array}$$

$$\begin{array}{r} 6 \\ + 7 \\ \hline \end{array} \qquad \begin{array}{r} 7 \\ + 4 \\ \hline \end{array} \qquad \begin{array}{r} 8 \\ + 9 \\ \hline \end{array} \qquad \begin{array}{r} 3 \\ + 7 \\ \hline \end{array} \qquad \begin{array}{r} 5 \\ + 3 \\ \hline \end{array}$$

$$\begin{array}{r} 4 \\ + 4 \\ \hline \end{array} \qquad \begin{array}{r} 6 \\ + 5 \\ \hline \end{array} \qquad \begin{array}{r} 3 \\ + 6 \\ \hline \end{array} \qquad \begin{array}{r} 8 \\ + 3 \\ \hline \end{array} \qquad \begin{array}{r} 7 \\ + 6 \\ \hline \end{array}$$

Score: _____

1-121Fa

Name •
(Draw an 8-centimeter line segment.)

Date _____

Day of the Week _____

1.  Write the number one hundred nine 3 more times.

2.  Colette had 7 pencils and 3 erasers. She gave Steven 2 pencils. Draw the pencils and erasers. Write a number sentence to show how many pencils she has now.

    ┌─────────────────────────────────────────────────────┐
    │                                                     │
    │                                                     │
    │                                                     │
    └─────────────────────────────────────────────────────┘

    Number sentence _____

    How many pencils does Colette have now? _____ pencils

3.  Measure these line segments using centimeters.

    ●━━━━━━━━━━━━━━━━━━━━━━━━━━━━━━━━━━━━━━━━━━━━━━━━●   _____ cm

    ●━━━━━━━━━━━━━━━━━━━━━━━●   _____ cm

4.  Draw lines to show how to divide the squares into fourths in two different ways. Color two fourths of each square.

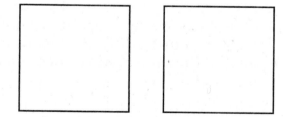

5.  Find the answers.

    $39 - 10 =$ ____       $61 - 10 =$ ____       $15 - 10 =$ ____

6.  Find the answers.

    $6 + 1 + 6 =$ ____              $3 + 5 + 7 =$ ____

1-121Wa

1.  Write the numbers that are **10** more than each number.

    5, _____          24, _____          73, _____

2.  Dana had 6 markers and 2 pencils. She gave her brother Josh 3 markers. Draw a picture and write a number sentence to show how many markers she has now.

    [ ]

    Number sentence _____

    How many markers does Dana have now? _____ markers

3.  The line segment below is 10 centimeters long.

    ●————————————————————————●

    Find something at home that is about 10 centimeters long. What did you find?

    _____

4.  Draw lines to show how to divide the squares into fourths in two different ways. Color one fourth of each square.

    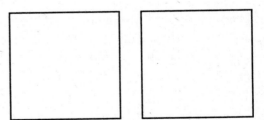

5.  Find the answers.

    62 − 10 = _____     47 − 10 = _____     13 − 10 = _____

6.  Find the answers.

    4 + 3 + 6 = _____          2 + 1 + 8 = _____

Name _____

| | | | | |
|---|---|---|---|---|
| 9<br>− 1 | 5<br>− 4 | 9<br>− 8 | 4<br>− 1 | 7<br>− 1 |
| 7<br>− 6 | 5<br>− 1 | 3<br>− 2 | 8<br>− 7 | 1<br>− 0 |
| 6<br>− 1 | 4<br>− 3 | 10<br>− 9 | 1<br>− 1 | 6<br>− 5 |
| 2<br>− 1 | 7<br>− 6 | 8<br>− 1 | 5<br>− 4 | 3<br>− 1 |
| 3<br>− 2 | 7<br>− 1 | 4<br>− 1 | 10<br>− 9 | 8<br>− 7 |

Score: _____

1-122Fa

Name ● _____
(Draw a 12-centimeter line segment.)

Date _____

Day of the Week _____

1.  Write the number one hundred ten 4 more times.

    110   110 - - - - - - - - - - - - - - - - - - - - - -

2.  Fred had 5 dimes and 3 pennies. His sister gave him 2 more dimes. Draw the coins.
    Color the pennies brown.

    

    How many dimes does Fred have now? _____ dimes

    How many pennies does Fred have now? _____ pennies

    How much money does he have altogether? _____ ¢

3.  Mrs. King lost two of her number cards for the numbers from 50 to 59.

    Which number cards did she lose? ☐ ☐

    | 59 | 52 | 55 | 50 | 56 | 51 | 54 | 57 |

4.  Find the answers.

    62 − 10 = ____       53 + 10 = ____       29 − 10 = ____

    2 + 7 + 3 = ____                5 + 1 + 6 = ____

5.  Find the total on each receipt.

    | 63 ¢ |        | 40 ¢ |        | 27 ¢ |
    | + 23 ¢ |      | + 19 ¢ |      | + 32 ¢ |
    | ☐ ¢ |         | ☐ ¢ |         | ☐ ¢ |

1. Circle the one that is different.

2. Neil had 4 dimes and 3 pennies. His brother gave him 3 more dimes. Draw the coins. Color the pennies brown.

How many dimes does Neil have now? _____ dimes

How many pennies does Neil have now? _____ pennies

How much money does he have altogether? _____ ¢

3. Mrs. Drenzek lost two of her number cards for the numbers from 60 to 69.

Which number cards did she lose?

| 63 | 65 | 69 | 61 | 68 | 64 | 66 | 60 |

4. Find the answers.

$89 - 10 =$ ____     $83 + 10 =$ ____     $24 - 10 =$ ____

$2 + 7 + 5 =$ ____          $6 + 7 + 1 =$ ____

5. Find the total on each receipt.

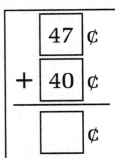

|        | 47 ¢ |
|--------|------|
| +      | 40 ¢ |
|        | ___ ¢ |

|        | 72 ¢ |
|--------|------|
| +      | 15 ¢ |
|        | ___ ¢ |

|        | 14 ¢ |
|--------|------|
| +      | 34 ¢ |
|        | ___ ¢ |

# Polygons

| 3 sides | 4 sides |
|---|---|
| | |

| 5 sides | 6 sides |
|---|---|
| | |

$$
\begin{array}{r} 9 \\ -1 \\ \hline \end{array}
\qquad
\begin{array}{r} 5 \\ -4 \\ \hline \end{array}
\qquad
\begin{array}{r} 9 \\ -8 \\ \hline \end{array}
\qquad
\begin{array}{r} 4 \\ -1 \\ \hline \end{array}
\qquad
\begin{array}{r} 7 \\ -1 \\ \hline \end{array}
$$

$$
\begin{array}{r} 7 \\ -6 \\ \hline \end{array}
\qquad
\begin{array}{r} 5 \\ -1 \\ \hline \end{array}
\qquad
\begin{array}{r} 3 \\ -2 \\ \hline \end{array}
\qquad
\begin{array}{r} 8 \\ -7 \\ \hline \end{array}
\qquad
\begin{array}{r} 1 \\ -0 \\ \hline \end{array}
$$

$$
\begin{array}{r} 6 \\ -1 \\ \hline \end{array}
\qquad
\begin{array}{r} 4 \\ -3 \\ \hline \end{array}
\qquad
\begin{array}{r} 10 \\ -9 \\ \hline \end{array}
\qquad
\begin{array}{r} 1 \\ -1 \\ \hline \end{array}
\qquad
\begin{array}{r} 6 \\ -5 \\ \hline \end{array}
$$

$$
\begin{array}{r} 2 \\ -1 \\ \hline \end{array}
\qquad
\begin{array}{r} 7 \\ -6 \\ \hline \end{array}
\qquad
\begin{array}{r} 8 \\ -1 \\ \hline \end{array}
\qquad
\begin{array}{r} 5 \\ -4 \\ \hline \end{array}
\qquad
\begin{array}{r} 3 \\ -1 \\ \hline \end{array}
$$

$$
\begin{array}{r} 3 \\ -2 \\ \hline \end{array}
\qquad
\begin{array}{r} 7 \\ -1 \\ \hline \end{array}
\qquad
\begin{array}{r} 4 \\ -1 \\ \hline \end{array}
\qquad
\begin{array}{r} 10 \\ -9 \\ \hline \end{array}
\qquad
\begin{array}{r} 8 \\ -7 \\ \hline \end{array}
$$

Score: _____

Name _____ •

(Draw an 11-centimeter line segment.)

Date _____

Day of the Week _____

1. Write the number one hundred eleven 5 more times.

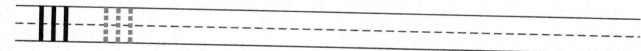

2. While she was away Shannon wrote four letters to her parents, four letters to her Aunt Debby, and two letters to her brother Billy. Draw a picture and write a number sentence to show the letters Shannon wrote.

Number sentence _____

How many letters did Shannon write? _____ letters

3. The children in Mrs. Mathew's class made this graph about their favorite ice cream.

Write two things you know about the children in Mrs. Matthew's class. (It's okay to use approximate spelling.)

1)_____

2)_____

4. Draw a four-sided polygon in the box.

5. Find the answers.

$$\begin{array}{r} 5 \\ 2 \\ +\ 3 \\ \hline \end{array} \qquad \begin{array}{r} 4 \\ 1 \\ +\ 4 \\ \hline \end{array} \qquad \begin{array}{r} 6 \\ 5 \\ +\ 4 \\ \hline \end{array}$$

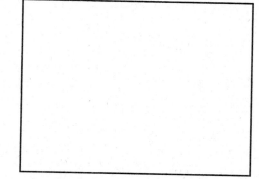

-123Wa

Name _____

1. Circle the two that are exactly the same.

2. While he was away, Billy wrote five letters to his parents, one letter to his Aunt Debby, and three letters to his sister Shannon. Draw a picture and write a number sentence to show the letters Billy wrote.

Number sentence _____

How many letters did Billy write? _____ letters

3. The children in Mrs. Brereton's class made this graph about their favorite fruit.

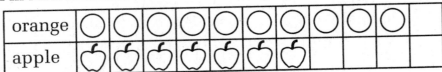

Write two things you know about the children in Mrs. Brereton's class. (It's okay to use approximate spelling.)

1) _____

2) _____

4. Draw a three-sided polygon in the box.

5. Find the answers.

$$\begin{array}{r} 9 \\ 9 \\ + 1 \\ \hline \end{array} \qquad \begin{array}{r} 3 \\ 2 \\ + 7 \\ \hline \end{array} \qquad \begin{array}{r} 4 \\ 3 \\ + 6 \\ \hline \end{array}$$

```
   2        3        5        8        6
 + 8      + 5      + 6      + 3      + 8
 ____     ____     ____     ____     ____


   3        7        1        6        4
 + 4      + 7      + 9      + 3      + 5
 ____     ____     ____     ____     ____


   5        6        3        9        8
 + 7      + 9      + 4      + 9      + 5
 ____     ____     ____     ____     ____


   6        7        8        3        5
 + 7      + 4      + 9      + 7      + 3
 ____     ____     ____     ____     ____


   4        6        3        8        7
 + 4      + 5      + 6      + 3      + 6
 ____     ____     ____     ____     ____
```

Score: _____

Name _____ •
(Draw a 9-centimeter line segment.)

Date _____

Day of the Week _____

1. Write the number one hundred twelve 4 more times.

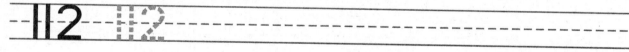

2. Walter counted the puzzle pieces. He had 2 piles of 10 pieces and 6 extra pieces. Draw a picture to show the 2 piles of 10 pieces and the 6 extra pieces.

How many pieces did Walter count? _____ pieces

3. Write a story for the number sentence **6 + 9 = 15**.

_____

_____

_____

4. Draw a six-sided polygon in the box.

5. How much money is this? _____

6. Find the answers.

   51 − 10 = ____     34 + 10 = ____

   2 + 7 + 8 = ____

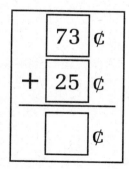

| | 73 | ¢ |
|---|---|---|
| + | 25 | ¢ |
| | | ¢ |

Name _____

1. Fill in the missing numbers.

| | | | | | 66 | | | | |
|---|---|---|---|---|---|---|---|---|---|
| | | | 74 | | | | | | |

2. Christopher counted the candies. He had 3 piles of 10 candies and 7 extra pieces. Draw a picture to show the 3 piles of 10 candies and the 7 extra pieces.

   How many candies did Christopher count? _____ candies

3. Write a story for the number sentence **3 + 4 = 7**.

   _____

   _____

   _____

4. Draw a five-sided polygon in the box.

5. How much money is this? _____

6. Find the answers.

   $62 - 10 =$ ____    $17 + 10 =$ ____

   $9 + 6 + 1 =$ ____

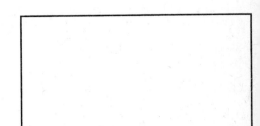

$$\begin{array}{r} 16\text{¢} \\ + 43\text{¢} \\ \hline \phantom{00}\text{¢} \end{array}$$

Name _____

Date _____

**1.** Write a story for the number sentence **6 + 4 = 10**.

_____

_____

_____

**2.** How much money is this? _____

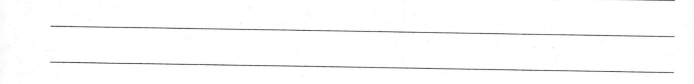

**3.** Color the spheres green.

Color the cubes yellow.

Color the cones red.

Color the cylinders blue.

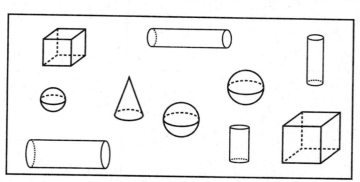

**4.** Color the graph to show how many cubes and cylinders you colored.

| Cubes |  |  |  |  |  |
|---|---|---|---|---|---|
| Cylinders |  |  |  |  |  |

How many more cylinders than cubes are there? _____

**5.** Count by 10's from 6. Fill in the numbers you say.

| 6 |  |  |  |  |  |  |  |  |  |
|---|---|---|---|---|---|---|---|---|---|

**6.** Fill in the answers.

$5 - 2 =$ _____    $10 - 3 =$ _____    $6 + 9 =$ _____    $5 + 3 =$ _____

11      5      7      11      9
− 5    − 2    − 4    − 6    − 5

7      9      5      7      11
− 4    − 4    − 3    − 3    − 5

9      11      7      11      5
− 5    − 5    − 4    − 6    − 2

9      5      11      9      7
− 4    − 3    − 5    − 5    − 3

5      7      9      11      5
− 2    − 3    − 4    − 6    − 3

Score: _____

Name _____ •
    (Draw an 8-centimeter line segment.)

Date _____

Day of the Week _____

1.  Write the number one hundred thirteen 3 more times.

    113  113 ------------------------------------------------

2.  Elizabeth has 2 dimes and 4 pennies. Stephanie has 1 penny and 5 dimes. Draw the coins. Color the pennies brown.

    How many dimes do the girls have altogether? _____ dimes

    How many pennies do the girls have altogether? _____ pennies

    How much money is that? _____

3.  The children in Mrs. Burton's class made this graph about their favorite colors.

    Write two things you know about the children in Mrs. Burton's class.

    1)_____

    _____

    2)_____

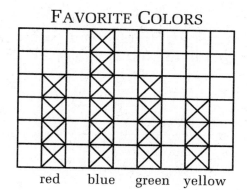

FAVORITE COLORS

red    blue    green    yellow

4.  Measure this line segment using inches.

    ●————————————●    _____ inches

5.  Measure this line segment using centimeters.

    ●————————————●    _____ centimeters

6.  Find the answers.

$$7 + 2 + 3 = \underline{\quad}$$

$$5 + 1 + 6 = \underline{\quad}$$

$$\begin{array}{r} 9 \\ -\ 4 \\ \hline \end{array} \qquad \begin{array}{r} 7 \\ -\ 3 \\ \hline \end{array} \qquad \begin{array}{r} 11 \\ -\ 6 \\ \hline \end{array} \qquad \begin{array}{r} 5 \\ -\ 2 \\ \hline \end{array}$$

1. Circle all the numbers that are between 38 and 51.

   43    55    50    35    47    39

2. Lesley has 3 dimes and 2 pennies. Theresa has 3 pennies and 1 dime. Draw the coins. Color the pennies brown.

   

   How many dimes do the girls have altogether? _____ dimes

   How many pennies do the girls have altogether? _____ pennies

   How much money is that? _____

3. The children in Mrs. Trembley's class made this graph about their favorite colors.

   Write two things you know about the children in Mrs. Trembley's class.

   _____

   _____

   _____

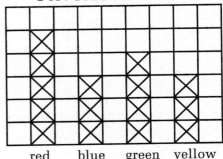

   red    blue    green    yellow

4. Finish the patterns.

   _____ , _____ , _____ , 400, 500, 600, _____ , _____ , _____

   23, 33, 43, _____ , _____ , _____ , _____ , _____

   50, 45, 40, _____ , _____ , _____ , _____ , _____

5. Find the answers.

   6 + 3 + 4 = _____

   3 + 1 + 4 = _____

   $$\begin{array}{r} 5 \\ -3 \\ \hline \end{array} \qquad \begin{array}{r} 9 \\ -5 \\ \hline \end{array} \qquad \begin{array}{r} 7 \\ -4 \\ \hline \end{array} \qquad \begin{array}{r} 11 \\ -5 \\ \hline \end{array}$$

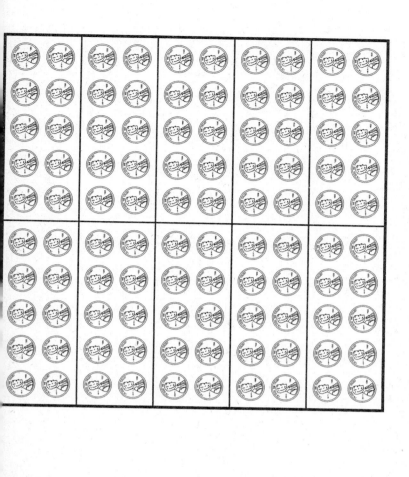

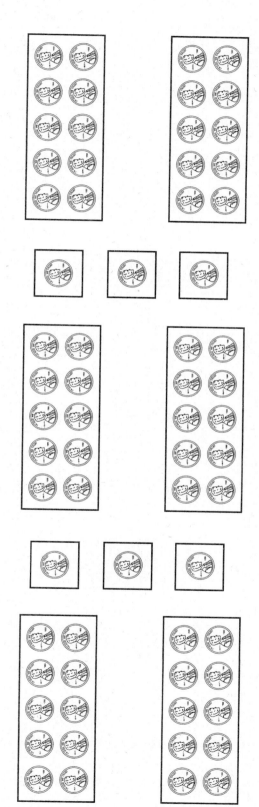

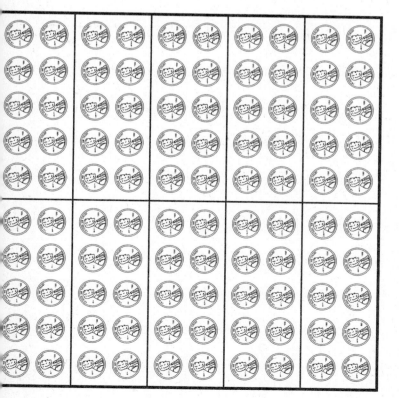

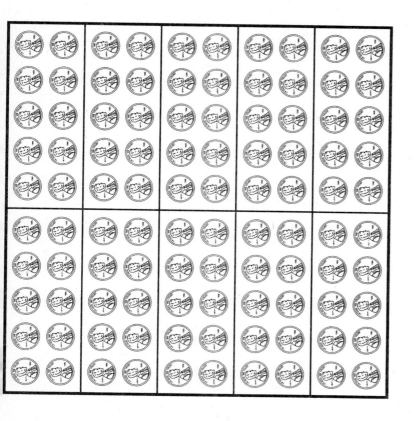

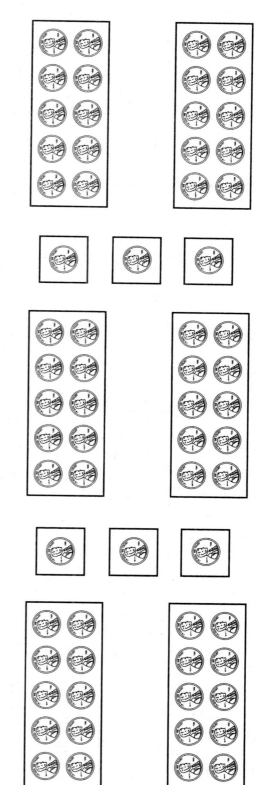

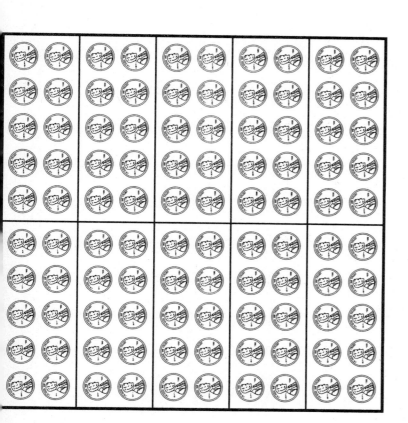

| | | | | |
|---|---|---|---|---|
| 11<br>− 5 | 5<br>− 2 | 7<br>− 4 | 11<br>− 6 | 9<br>− 5 |
| 7<br>− 4 | 9<br>− 4 | 5<br>− 3 | 7<br>− 3 | 11<br>− 5 |
| 9<br>− 5 | 11<br>− 5 | 7<br>− 4 | 11<br>− 6 | 5<br>− 2 |
| 9<br>− 4 | 5<br>− 3 | 11<br>− 5 | 9<br>− 5 | 7<br>− 3 |
| 5<br>− 2 | 7<br>− 3 | 9<br>− 4 | 11<br>− 6 | 5<br>− 3 |

Score: _____

Name •
     (Draw a 4-inch line segment.)

Date _____

Day of the Week _____

1. Write the number one hundred fourteen 3 more times.

    114   114

2. Five children from Room 4 went to the nurse's office to have their eyes checked. Six children from Room 5 went to the nurse's office to have their eyes checked. Draw a picture and write a number sentence to show the children at the nurse's office.

    ┌────────────────────────────────────────────┐
    │                                              │
    │                                              │
    └────────────────────────────────────────────┘

Number sentence _____

How many children are at the nurse's office? _____ children

3. The children in Mrs. Flinter's class made this graph about their favorite insects. Write two things you know about the children in Mrs. Flinter's class.

    1)_____

    _____

    2)_____

FAVORITE INSECTS

Ladybug

Firefly

Ant

4. Color the pennies brown. How much money is this? _____

5. Find the answers.

    $2 + 2 + 7 =$ _____

    $5 + 4 + 4 =$ _____

$$\begin{array}{r} 9 \\ -8 \\ \hline \end{array} \qquad \begin{array}{r} 8 \\ -1 \\ \hline \end{array} \qquad \begin{array}{r} 5 \\ -2 \\ \hline \end{array} \qquad \begin{array}{r} 6 \\ -5 \\ \hline \end{array} \qquad \begin{array}{r} 8 \\ -2 \\ \hline \end{array}$$

-126Wa

1.  Finish the number patterns.

    100, 200, 300, _____ , _____ , _____ , _____ , _____

    19, 17, 15, _____ , _____ , _____ , _____ , _____

2.  Six children from Room 5 went to the library to return books. Seven children from Room 4 went to the library to return books. Draw a picture and write a number sentence to show the children in the library.

    ┌─────────────────────────────────────────────┐
    │                                             │
    │                                             │
    │                                             │
    └─────────────────────────────────────────────┘

    Number sentence _____

    How many children are in the library? _____ children

3.  The children in Miss Rocco's class made this graph about their favorite insects. Write two things you know about the children in Miss Rocco's class.

    FAVORITE INSECTS

    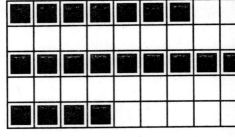

    1)_____

    _____

    2)_____

4.  Color the pennies brown. How much money is this? _____

5.  Find the answers.

    3 + 3 + 6 = _____

    2 + 5 + 5 = _____

$$\begin{array}{r} 7 \\ -1 \\ \hline \end{array} \qquad \begin{array}{r} 5 \\ -4 \\ \hline \end{array} \qquad \begin{array}{r} 9 \\ -2 \\ \hline \end{array} \qquad \begin{array}{r} 7 \\ -6 \\ \hline \end{array} \qquad \begin{array}{r} 6 \\ -2 \\ \hline \end{array}$$

| 11 | 5 | 7 | 11 | 9 |
|---|---|---|---|---|
| − 5 | − 2 | − 4 | − 6 | − 5 |

| 7 | 9 | 5 | 7 | 11 |
|---|---|---|---|---|
| − 4 | − 4 | − 3 | − 3 | − 5 |

| 9 | 11 | 7 | 11 | 5 |
|---|---|---|---|---|
| − 5 | − 5 | − 4 | − 6 | − 2 |

| 9 | 5 | 11 | 9 | 7 |
|---|---|---|---|---|
| − 4 | − 3 | − 5 | − 5 | − 3 |

| 5 | 7 | 9 | 11 | 5 |
|---|---|---|---|---|
| − 2 | − 3 | − 4 | − 6 | − 3 |

core: _____

Name ● 
(Draw a 12-centimeter line segment.)

Date _____

Day of the Week _____

1. Write the number one hundred fifteen 4 more times.

2. There are nine boys and seven girls in Mrs. Glenn's class. Color the graph to show the number of boys and girls in Mrs. Glenn's class.

CHILDREN IN MRS. GLENN'S CLASS

| Girls | | | | | | | | | |
|---|---|---|---|---|---|---|---|---|---|
| Boys | | | | | | | | | |

How many more boys than girls are there? _____

How many children are in the class altogether? _____ children

3. Write a story for the number sentence **9 − 2 = 7**.

   _____

   _____

   _____

4. Show **8:30** on the clock.

5. Find the answers.

   $2 + 6 + 8 =$ _____      $7 - 4 =$ _____

   $1 + 6 + 1 =$ _____      $11 - 5 =$ _____

6. Find the answers.

$$\begin{array}{r} 79¢ \\ + 10¢ \\ \hline ¢ \end{array} \qquad \begin{array}{r} 65¢ \\ + 23¢ \\ \hline ¢ \end{array} \qquad \begin{array}{r} 43¢ \\ + 41¢ \\ \hline ¢ \end{array} \qquad \begin{array}{r} 30¢ \\ + 28¢ \\ \hline ¢ \end{array}$$

1. Color all the congruent shapes yellow.

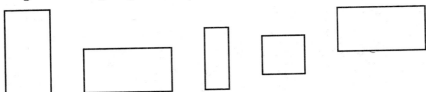

2. There are six boys and eight girls in Mrs. Smolder's class. Color the graph to show the number of boys and girls in Mrs. Smolder's class.

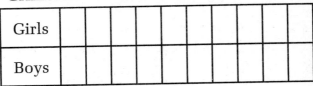

| CHILDREN IN MRS. SMOLDER'S CLASS | | | | | | | | | | |
|---|---|---|---|---|---|---|---|---|---|---|
| Girls | | | | | | | | | | |
| Boys | | | | | | | | | | |

How many more girls than boys are there? _____

How many children are in the class altogether? _____ children

3. Write a story for the number sentence **10 − 6 = 4**.

_____

_____

_____

4. Show **11:30** on the clock.

5. Find the answers.

$3 + 5 + 7 =$ ____    $9 − 5 =$ ____

$2 + 6 + 8 =$ ____    $7 − 3 =$ ____

6. Find the answers.

| 10¢ | 54¢ | 32¢ | 11¢ |
|---|---|---|---|
| + 82¢ | + 24¢ | + 37¢ | + 85¢ |
| ____ ¢ | ____ ¢ | ____ ¢ | ____ ¢ |

| 6 | 8 | 9 | 7 | 9 |
|---|---|---|---|---|
| − 4 | − 3 | − 6 | − 5 | − 3 |

| 8 | 6 | 8 | 9 | 8 |
|---|---|---|---|---|
| − 6 | − 4 | − 5 | − 6 | − 3 |

| 7 | 9 | 8 | 6 | 7 |
|---|---|---|---|---|
| − 5 | − 3 | − 5 | − 4 | − 5 |

| 8 | 8 | 9 | 9 | 8 |
|---|---|---|---|---|
| − 6 | − 3 | − 6 | − 3 | − 6 |

| 6 | 7 | 9 | 8 | 9 |
|---|---|---|---|---|
| − 4 | − 5 | − 3 | − 5 | − 6 |

Score: _____

Name _____ •
    (Draw a 4-inch line segment.)

Date _____

Day of the Week _____

1. Write the number one hundred sixteen 3 more times.

2. On Mrs. Barlow's lunch graph, eight children put their tags in the lunch from home row. Six children put their tags in the school lunch row. Draw the tags on the lunch graph.

| Lunch from home | |
|---|---|
| School lunch | |

How many more children eat home lunch than eat school lunch? _____

How many tags are on the graph? _____ tags

3. Draw a five-sided polygon in the box.

4. How much money is this? _____

5. Maureen wrote a two-digit number on a piece of paper.
She gave the children the following clues to help them guess her secret number.
Maureen said, "The digits I used are 4 and 6."

Write the two possible numbers. _____  _____

Maureen said, "The number is between 48 and 70." Circle Maureen's secret number.

6. Find the answers.

$$6 + 7 + 3 = \underline{\quad} \qquad 8 + 1 + 9 = \underline{\quad} \qquad 2 + 7 + 8 = \underline{\quad}$$

1. Circle all the numbers that are between 50 and 75.

| 78 | 43 | 61 | 58 | 82 | 71 |
|----|----|----|----|----|----|

2. On Mrs. York's lunch graph, nine children put their tags in the lunch from home row. Six children put their tags in the school lunch row. Draw the tags on the lunch graph.

| Lunch from home | |
|-----------------|--|
| School lunch | |

How many more children eat home lunch than eat school lunch? _____

How many tags are on the graph? _____ tags

3. Draw a three-sided polygon in the box.

4. How much money is this? _____

5. Sharon wrote a two-digit number on a piece of paper.
She gave the children the following clues to help them guess her secret number.
Sharon said, "The digits I used are 7 and 9."

Write the two possible numbers. _____    _____

Sharon said, "The number is between 75 and 95." Circle Sharon's secret number.

6. Find the answers.

   8 + 2 + 6 = ____    5 + 4 + 7 = ____    2 + 9 + 3 = ____

|  6   |  8   |  9   |  7   |  9   |
| ---- | ---- | ---- | ---- | ---- |
| − 4  | − 3  | − 6  | − 5  | − 3  |

|  8   |  6   |  8   |  9   |  8   |
| ---- | ---- | ---- | ---- | ---- |
| − 6  | − 4  | − 5  | − 6  | − 3  |

|  7   |  9   |  8   |  6   |  7   |
| ---- | ---- | ---- | ---- | ---- |
| − 5  | − 3  | − 5  | − 4  | − 5  |

|  8   |  8   |  9   |  9   |  8   |
| ---- | ---- | ---- | ---- | ---- |
| − 6  | − 3  | − 6  | − 3  | − 6  |

|  6   |  7   |  9   |  8   |  9   |
| ---- | ---- | ---- | ---- | ---- |
| − 4  | − 5  | − 3  | − 5  | − 6  |

Score: _____

1-129Fa

Name _____ .
    (Draw a 10-centimeter line segment.)

Date _____

Day of the Week _____

**1.** Write the number one hundred seventeen 4 more times.

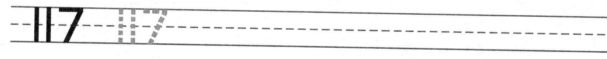

**2.** In Room 9, ten children wore long sleeve shirts and seven children wore short sleeve shirts. Color the graph to show the shirts the children wore.

| Short sleeves | | | | | | | | | |
|---|---|---|---|---|---|---|---|---|---|
| Long sleeves | | | | | | | | | |

How many more children wore long sleeves than wore short sleeves? _____

How many children are in Room 9? _____ children

**3.** Measure this line segment using centimeters.

_____ centimeters

**4.** Measure this line segment using inches.

_____ inches

**5.** Circle all of the shapes divided into fourths. Color two fourths of each circled shape blue.

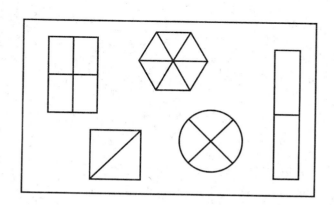

**6.** Find the answers.

$$
\begin{array}{r} 52¢ \\ + 34¢ \\ \hline ¢ \end{array}
\qquad
\begin{array}{r} 10¢ \\ + 89¢ \\ \hline ¢ \end{array}
\qquad
\begin{array}{r} 25¢ \\ + 42¢ \\ \hline ¢ \end{array}
\qquad
\begin{array}{r} 13¢ \\ + 73¢ \\ \hline ¢ \end{array}
$$

1-129Wa

Name _____

1.  Write these numbers in order from least to greatest.

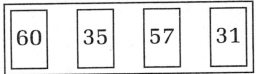    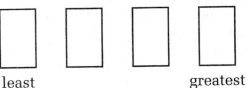

least                                    greatest

2.  In Room 8, six children wore sandals and ten children wore sneakers. Color the graph to show what shoes the children wore.

| Sneakers | | | | | | | | | | |
|---|---|---|---|---|---|---|---|---|---|---|
| Sandals | | | | | | | | | | |

How many more children wore sneakers than sandals? _____

How many children are in Room 8? _____ children

3.  Find the answers.

    9 − 8 = _____     9 − 5 = _____     7 − 2 = _____     11 − 6 = _____

    5 + 7 = _____     8 + 3 = _____     6 + 8 = _____     7 + 4 = _____

4.  Find the answers.

    42 − 10 = _____     37 + 10 = _____     25 − 10 = _____

5.  Circle all of the shapes divided into halves. Color one half of each circled shape.

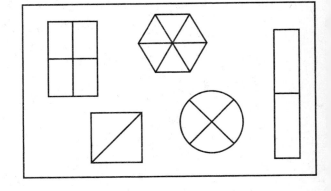

6.  Find the answers.

$$\begin{array}{r} 21¢ \\ + 25¢ \\ \hline ¢ \end{array} \qquad \begin{array}{r} 17¢ \\ + 62¢ \\ \hline ¢ \end{array} \qquad \begin{array}{r} 38¢ \\ + 30¢ \\ \hline ¢ \end{array} \qquad \begin{array}{r} 24¢ \\ + 44¢ \\ \hline ¢ \end{array}$$

Name _____

Date _____

**LESSON 130**

*Math 1*

1. Two children from Room 1 went to the library. Six children from Room 3 went to the library. Draw a picture and write a number sentence to show the children in the library.

   _____

   Number sentence _____

   How many children are at the library now? _____ children

2. Draw a five-sided polygon in the box.

3. How much money is this? _____

4. Find the answers.

   $25 - 10 =$ _____      $49 - 10 =$ _____

   $2 + 6 + 8 =$ _____      $3 + 2 + 7 =$ _____

5. Measure this line segment using centimeters. _____ centimeters

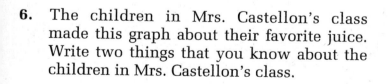

6. The children in Mrs. Castellon's class made this graph about their favorite juice. Write two things that you know about the children in Mrs. Castellon's class.

   FAVORITE JUICE

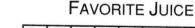

   1) _____

   _____

   2) _____

   _____

Copyright by Saxon Publishers, Inc. and Nancy Larson. Reproduction prohibited.